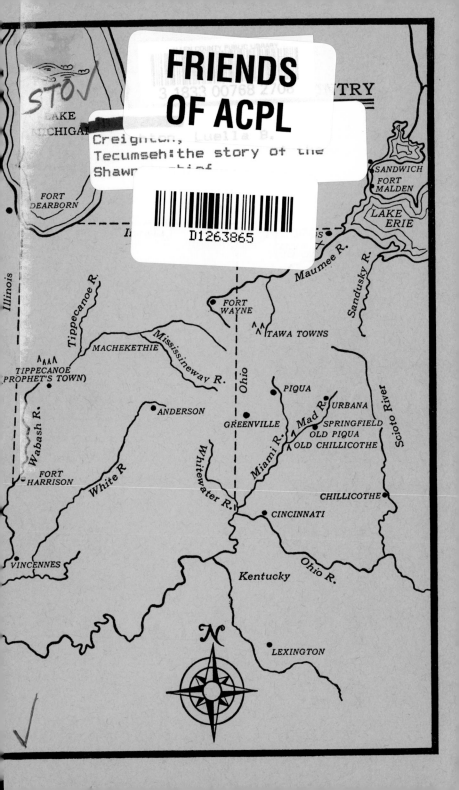

FRIENDS
OF ACPL

3 1833 00768 2766

Creighton, Luella B.
Tecumseh:the story of the
Shawnee chief

D1263865

STO✓

LAKE
MICHIGAN

FORT
DEARBORN

Illinois

Tippecanoe R.

MACHEKETHIE

Mississineway R.

TIPPECANOE
(PROPHET'S TOWN)

Wabash R.

ANDERSON

FORT
HARRISON

White R.

Whitewater R.

VINCENNES

Kentucky

SANDWICH
FORT
MALDEN

LAKE
ERIE

Maumee R.

Sandusky R.

FORT
WAYNE

TAWA TOWNS

Ohio

PIQUA

URBANA

GREENVILLE

Mad R.

SPRINGFIELD
OLD PIQUA
OLD CHILLICOTHE

Miami R.

Scioto River

CHILLICOTHE

CINCINNATI

Ohio R.

LEXINGTON

N

GREAT STORIES OF CANADA

TECUMSEH

GREAT STORIES OF CANADA

Many other titles in preparation

Tecumseh

THE STORY OF THE SHAWNEE CHIEF

By LUELLA BRUCE CREIGHTON

Illustrated by William Lytle

NEW YORK : ST. MARTIN'S PRESS
1965

© LUELLA BRUCE CREIGHTON, 1965

All rights reserved – no part of this book may be reproduced in any form without permission in writing from the publisher, except by a reviewer who wishes to quote brief passages in connection with a review written for inclusion in a magazine or newspaper.

Library of Congress Catalogue Card No. 65-20417

PRINTED IN CANADA

U. S. 1322787

To Angus and Stephen

Contents

TECUMSEH

1. A Shawnee Is Born

A son was born at Old Piqua on the Mad River, to the gentle Shawnee chief Puckeshinwa and Methoataske, his wife. The child's mother was a passionate, violent, and vengeful woman. Her first hate and her last were for the pale-face. She breathed her hatred into the ears of her many children.

The tribe had not been long in the peaceful, fertile valley of the Mad in 1768 when this boy was born. The Shawnee were on a great, leisurely migration then, from the Alabama country towards the Scioto River. The migrations were deliberate journeys. Sometimes the Shawnee would settle for several years in one place; the squaws would plant the corn, mounding up the hills with their little hoes of turtle-shells or horn. Then they would move on again, thinking as they went that the news would drive their enemies away. "The Shawnee, the greatest among the Indian nations, journey northwards now."

The valley of the Mad, a little stream that flows into the Miami and thence into the beautiful Ohio, the Indians' most beloved river, was rich and beautiful. No need on the Mad to plant the little fertilizing fish called alewives with each hill of corn; the corn goddess did not need this propitiation here. Beans climbed the cornstalks, and pumpkins grew fat and golden in the rows between. The river-bottoms stretching as far as even an Indian eye could see offered thousands of acres of fertility.

The Mad was a gentle river, full of fish. There was game in abundance in the forests beyond. It was a wonderful place for the braves, the squaws, and the children. In the valley of the lovely Ohio the Shawnee felt that they had finally come home. The land south of the Ohio they considered to be their own hunting-grounds. Here they grew to be the largest Indian nation in Ohio.

The problem of naming the new child faced his parents. He was the fifth child – the third son – of a Shawnee chief. Cheeseekau and Sauwaseekau were his elder brothers. Perhaps this new son might grow to be a chief, like his father. To be a Shawnee chief, in the eyes of the Shawnee, was to be great above all men. For the Shawnee were proud and fierce, created from the head and brain of the Master of Life. Pale-faces, English and French and Dutch, had been made later, from His chest and hands and feet.

After grave consideration they named the baby "nila ni tha'mthka". The Shawnee name meant "I cross somebody's path". Methoataske meant her son to be as a panther leaping on the pale-face, destroying him utterly. The swiftest leap of all, the flash of a star half-way across the heavens, was a vivid parallel, in the Shawnee imagining. So the leaping heavenly panther became a meteor. The baby was named Tecumseh – "Shooting Star".

Legends of Shawnee greatness were bedtime stories for the young Tecumseh. The Shawnee were an offshoot of the Delawares, whom the French called the "Wolves". They had travelled south. When their kinsmen in the Miami were threatened by the Iroquois, who meant to push them out of the favoured Ohio valley, they called on their tribesmen for help. Up from Georgia and Carolina the Shawnee leapt, dancing their unique and terrible dance at every stopping-place. The braves were ripe for war when they reached the St. Joseph River. Here in deep fog they allowed the Iroquois to pursue them. Then they stepped softly off the trail and, when the warriors had passed, fell on them from behind and slaughtered them.

Tecumseh listened and remembered. He forgot nothing. He could see the cleverness of the ruse – to lead the enemy on and then, in his hour of expected victory, to snatch it from him.

From many of the legends there was something to learn, for a boy who would be a chief, perhaps, one day. From some there seemed nothing but stupidity. The story of the "Battle of the Grasshoppers" was one of these.

It was deep summer and the blackberries were ripening. The women of the Shawnee and the Delaware squaws were picking berries under the hot sun. Bees bumbled about the bushes, thorns scratched brown skins, and the great green grasshoppers of the summer meadows leapt among the pickers. The children reached out their hands and caught them, holding them tightly to see if they would spit tobacco juice into their clenched fists. One mighty grasshopper, the king of them all, leapt, and two papooses – one a Delaware, the other a Shawnee – scrambled after him as he landed. They rolled in anger, each determined to have the hopper. Fists and teeth came into play.

A Delaware mother and a Shawnee mother ran to the aid of their offspring. Delaware children fought Shawnee children, Delaware mothers fought Shawnee mothers. Shrieks of anger, mother against mother, reached the ears of the braves, who were lounging in the sun. Tomahawks and scalping-knives flashed, and the Delaware and Shawnee were at war.

When the light failed, the field was strewn with bodies. Delaware scalps hung from Shawnee belts. But most of the men who lay scalped in the meadow grass were Shawnee, and it was the Shawnee who were forced to retreat from the field.

Tecumseh's steady hazel eyes saw little to approve in the Battle of the Grasshoppers. There was no honour in it, for tribe or Indian.

Five years before Tecumseh was born, a Royal Proclamation had closed "to any purchases of settlements" the immense region between the Alleghenies and the Mississippi, from Florida to Quebec. But in those five years 30,000 white settlers had crossed the mountains, and land companies were formed. The Virginians were invading the Ohio lands, which the Indians had every right to believe were theirs. The Virginians claimed that the southern part of Ohio was really theirs, by earlier charter.

Since the end of the Pontiac war, in 1763, the Shawnee had kept the peace. Cornstalk, the great Shawnee war chief, had lifted no tomahawk, and his braves kept their scalping-knives clean. The Shawnee stayed at home; the tomahawk slept, waiting in the wigwams.

Then, in 1774, when Tecumseh was six, the Virginians began to cross the Ohio, invading the Shawnee land. Cornstalk sounded the war drums. Smoke signals rose from the hills, and the sinister music of the Shawnee war dance split the quiet of the forest.

Delaware and Mingo and Wyandot joined the Shawnee. The greatest of the fighting chiefs, seasoned and tough – Red Hawk, Blue Jacket, the famous Shawnee Logan, and Tecumseh's father Puckeshinwa – fought under Cornstalk.

Before the battle Puckeshinwa called Cheeseekau, his eldest son, to him. The chief felt the strange premonition of death which many Shawnee had known. "I shall not come back," he said. "I feel the stiffening of death beginning. See to the rearing of your brothers. Let them be made fearless in war, and wise in victory."

Cornstalk suffered defeat after long fighting, in a brilliantly deployed battle at Point Pleasant on the Kanawha. Many braves and many Americans were dead at the end.

The Indians called these sword-bearing cavalry, and the American infantry with bayonets, the Long Knives.

Yet Puckeshinwa lived still, and came again to the Mad River. Within a few days of his return he met a band of white hunters who demanded arrogantly that he should be their guide. Puckeshinwa saw the blood of Indians red on their hands. "No!" he said. A white hunter drew his pistol and shot Puckeshinwa through the breast. "Insolent savage!"

Methoataske waited in the village for the hunter who did not return. As night came down she called for Tecumseh and together they searched in the forest for the chief. He was almost dead when they found him. He had life and breath for only one message: "Behold the faith of white men."

Wild grief and fury possessed Methoataske. The sound of her lamentations pierced the silence of the wood. Mother and son gazed down at the dead man. "Vengeance," the widow whispered hoarsely, "you shall be avenged." She laid her hand on the little boy's head. "You shall avenge the death of your father the chief. Your feet shall be swift as forked lightning, your arm shall be as the thunderbolt. When the strength of your manhood is come then your enemies shall hear your name and tremble."

For three years, at the anniversary of the murder, his mother brought Tecumseh to his father's grave, uttered prophecy, and sang of revenge. She imbued the boy with bitter hatred for every pale-face. "Their souls are dark in treachery, their hands are red in blood. They met your father alone on his hills and killed him. Avenge!"

Long before Tecumseh was fully grown his mother left him for ever. She drifted back to her own people, the Creek, in the south, taking one of her daughters with her. Her totem was the turtle, and like the turtle, which lays its eggs in the sand and then wanders off, she deserted her family. Her elder daughter, Tecumapease, was left with the responsibility of mothering Tecumseh and of rearing Laulewasika, a cross-grained fat child, "Loud Mouth", born a few months after his father's death.

Methoataske had fashioned an instrument of hate for the white men in her gifted son Tecumseh. She felt that her task was done.

It was October 1774 and winter was coming fast. Although the great chiefs who had followed Cornstalk into battle at Point Pleasant had survived it, the scattered villages could not be protected from attack. Americans were confidently raiding Shawnee villages on the Scioto and the Miami. Women and children would suffer if the war went on. Chief Cornstalk was forced to make a painful peace with the Americans.

The majestic Cornstalk, a man of great dignity and composure, a brilliant orator, and a mighty warrior, became Tecumseh's hero. Fatherless, he looked to Cornstalk and learned courage.

It was not easy to keep the Shawnee from fighting after Point Pleasant. They saw the flat-boats laden with guns and blankets and sugar and tea float down the Ohio with only a few men on board. But Cornstalk kept the Shawnee from breaking the peace. It would be shattered by the pale-face, not the Indian, if it was going to break.

There was provocation in plenty. The year after the American-Shawnee agreement, the Americans were fighting the British. The Thirteen Council Fires of the Americans had declared war against their mother country. Cornstalk had given his word that the Shawnee would not fight the Americans, and the war chief had decided that they were not to be drawn into the war on the other side, either.

From time to time Cornstalk warned the Americans of the drift of the Ohio Indians to the British. The Americans asked Cornstalk to make a contour map of the Ohio valley for them. He went with two braves to Point Pleasant, that place of fearful memories, and in a cabin there he drew the map, showing every rise and stream. For to the Shawnee the Ohio valley was as his ploughed fields are to the farmer. He drew the map on the floor of the cabin, showing the land north of the Ohio, and marked the western rivers on it. The young Shawnee chiefs Red Hawk and Cornstalk's son Ellinipsico joined the map-maker at Point Pleasant.

On this day a white man was killed along the Ohio. Warning came to Cornstalk that the murder was being laid to him, that white soldiers were approaching Point Pleasant, and that Ellinipsico would be charged with bringing hostile Indians into the camp. Cornstalk had been busy making his map when the white man was murdered, and the only Indian with Ellinipsico was Red Hawk.

Perhaps Cornstalk should have fled upon the warning. But he could not see how he could be charged with murdering a white man miles away.

When a mob of white soldiers swarmed to the cabin he strode to the door and stood there in the full majesty of a righteous man. "My son," he said, "the Great Spirit has seen fit that we should die together. He has sent you here that His will be fulfilled. Let us submit."

Cornstalk was shot down with seven bullets. Ellinipsico received his rain of bullets as he watched by his father's body. The shooting of Red Hawk and the two braves completed the irresponsible mass murder.

So Cornstalk died, and the Shawnee were released from their bond. Five years of Shawnee war – bloody massacre, burning, and outrage – followed Cornstalk's murder. No flat-boat was safe on the Ohio.

Chief Blackfish claimed Tecumseh's next allegiance. He was an amiable and tyrannical chief, quick to anger and quick to laugh. He ruled Old Chillicothe, the Shawnee town on the Mad, south of Old Piqua. Hot vengeance in his heart for Cornstalk, Blackfish sent his raiding parties like swarms of bees into the Kentucky country. When Tecumseh was nine years old Blackfish adopted him.

Every Indian chief was always on the look-out for good boys to add to his family; the squaws did not bear enough sons. Indians needed manpower; a boy was always welcome in an Indian camp. Many white boys taken as prisoners were adopted as sons by their captors. In Tecumseh's own boyhood at least three white boys became his foster-brothers.

A white boy chosen to be an Indian brave passed through a ritual of initiation. He was taken to the river and the rites were held there. Ceremonial scrubbing was given to him, to wash out the white man's blood and change it into Indian blood. A hair-plucking followed. The Indians found the hair on the face and body of the white man a revolting sight. A solemn ceremony in the Council House completed the little prisoner's ordeal. Sometimes these boys did become almost like Indians, and forsook their white heritage completely. Some escaped and went back to their own people.

Stephen Ruddell, an English boy, became Tecumseh's foster-brother and lived for fifteen years in the Shawnee camp. He was Tecumseh's lifelong friend, the best inter-

preter the Shawnee had. He married into the tribe, took the
Indian name Sinnamatha – "Big Fish" – and acknowledged
no allegiance to the whites.

That strange man Daniel Boone was for three months a
son of Blackfish, brother of Tecumseh. The Indian boy
watched with constant curiosity this first grown-up white
man he had ever known. Boone had killed Blackfish's son,
but still Blackfish was fascinated by him, as by some exotic
pet. He had the run of the camp.

The Shawnee gave their boys a kind of formal schooling.
Out under the trees an experienced, knowledgeable old brave
taught Shawnee principles to the children, besides the prac-
tical, useful handcrafts, the theories of hunting, and the
practice of oratory. They were taught to honour their elders

and to remember and respect those who had died an honourable death. Tecumseh's phenomenal memory recorded for ever the stories of battle, of victory and defeat, of treaty and contract, made and broken by the Americans.

Blackfish instructed his boys in the swift assault, the sudden swoop of a war party down upon an unsuspecting enemy. Where no one seemed to be, Blackfish could suddenly appear. He taught his boys that victory is not necessarily won by superior numbers, or superior ammunition. Surprise, swiftness, the heart that will not consider the possibility of defeat – these are the elements of success in war. Kentucky, across the Ohio, lived in constant terror of Blackfish and his warriors.

Winter and summer, the mock battles went on, the training and the hardening of the Indian boys. War dances were learned, wrestling in snow perfected, mock scalpings made. The tomahawk and the scalping-knife, the bow and arrow, had to be made to answer to the hand of the Indian child. Tecumseh at this time held the rifle in contempt. He could do just as well, or better, with his arrow. And the swift song of the arrow did not frighten the game from the hunting-grounds as the crack of the rifle did.

Blackfish determined to attack the Kentucky town of Boonesville, while Daniel Boone was still a prisoner in the Indian camp. Boone slipped away from a Shawnee hunting expedition and warned the settlers that Blackfish was coming.

Nearly five hundred warriors, glorious in plumes and paint, moved down towards Boonesville under Blackfish, to wrest the town from the "Kentucks". Ten days later Tecumseh saw the defeated warriors glide back into Old Chillicothe. Blackfish's kind of warfare, the bush-whacking surprise and attack, would not do for major engagements. The old chief knew, too, that his pet, Boone, had betrayed his intentions. His whole attitude to his captives changed from this time on. When the time came to hand out justice to another white man, Simon Kenton, there was no mercy.

Kenton was caught in the act of stealing all of Blackfish's horses from the horse pound. He had to run the Shawnee gauntlet eight times in punishment. The evening before, the gauntlet-running Kenton was tied to a stake, and the squaws tore at him with their claws until there was not a thread of clothing left on his white body. The children howled about him and lashed at him with their pointed sticks. They let him rest then in a well-guarded hut for better sport in the morning. The scalp of the friend who had been with him hung on the door.

Two lines of Indians formed the gauntlet. It ran eleven yards short of half a mile for Kenton before he could reach the safety of the Council House. Braves, squaws, children, all armed with knives, tomahawks, hoes, clubs, and switches, waited for him. The drums beat a measure, and he was forced

to start. The squaws were more fierce than the braves in the gauntlet. They were not permitted to fight in battles, but they vented their wild, blood-thirsty fury in the gauntlet.

The racial memory of a thousand years of traditional punishment and torture for prisoners boiled in Tecumseh's blood. He danced and shouted and hooted derision at the pain and anguish of the white man. He laughed to see the misery in his face, the awful helplessness before his tormentor, the blood streaming down his back from the lash of Blackfish's heavy hickory switch. He was ten years old.

When Kenton came, still living, to the Council House after running the gauntlet eight times, they tied him to a wild horse, which was whipped through the woods, dragging him over the ground and banging him against the trees. He was still alive even after that. The Shawnee decided to let him live.

It would have been better for them if they had killed him. When, two years later, the Kentuckians planned a great expedition to destroy the Indian towns, Kenton showed them the way.

Word came to Old Chillicothe that the whites were coming. The Shawnee put the village to the flames. When the men from Kentucky arrived there was nothing there but smoking ruin. The Kentuckians went on to Old Piqua. Bows and arrows even in the hands of the best braves are useless against artillery and rifles. The women and children snatched what possessions they could carry and fled. The fort and the houses went down. Arrow-shooting Indians to the west of the town kept a gap open so that the old and young and the women could pass through. Suddenly, at sundown, the fighting Indians, all the Indians, vanished. When the leader of the Kentucks, George Rogers Clark, came to the town there was no one there at all. Clark put the village to the torch. Old Piqua, houses and fort, cabins and wigwams, five hundred acres of corn in tassel, blazed. Then there were only smouldering ashes where once Tecumseh's home had stood. Three miles along the Mad River the fire raged, rose and fell, and the hot ashes blew over the water.

The smouldering hate in the Shawnee hearts was hotter than the ashes of Old Piqua. Tecumseh escaped through the woods, the memory of his mother's words running through his head like a song. The Americans had laid a heavy burden on his shoulders.

For four nights the Shawnee funeral dirges rose wailing through the forest. Then the Shawnee roused themselves to cross the Miami, and on its hospitable west bank they built a new Piqua.

2. First Blood

THE REVOLUTION that separated the Thirteen Colonies from their mother country was over. But the war in the west, Kentucky against Shawnee, still went on its bloody course. Clark again and again crossed the Ohio with his torch.

Big Ben Logan, a giant Kentucky colonel, camped with his troops at the place where the Mad River meets the Miami. Here the Shawnee attacked him. Tecumseh went with his brother Cheeseekau into the fight. Cheeseekau fell wounded and Tecumseh fled the field. Thus Tecumseh, gun-shy at fourteen, joined that band of great warriors, white and red, who have run in terror from their first battlefield.

It was only a skirmish; Cheeseekau was not severely wounded and sat with the warriors at the campfire that night. Tecumseh, sick with shame, hung his head and waited for his reproof. One brave was praised for prowess, one for courage. Tecumseh waited. The memories of his grand conceit, his mighty vows, his grandiose schemes for revenge whirled in his head.

One by one the chiefs spoke. The fire burned and went out. The chiefs and braves rose and went back to their dwellings. There was no word for Tecumseh, no reproach, no shaming. He was left alone in the company of his own shame, by the embers of the fire. The reproof was complete.

He never turned his back on danger again.

After Cornstalk's death, Blackfish's Shawnee had so harassed the flat-boat traffic that they had all but stopped navigation on the Ohio. But the settlers, and those who were provisioning the settlers, had to travel by water if they were to come through at all with their goods.

Two years after Tecumseh's flight from the guns of Big Ben Logan, he had his first chance at a flat-boat adventure.

Two flat-boats lashed together floated in their clumsy fashion down the Ohio. From a look-out in the branches of a tall maple, watchers kept their eyes on the boat. Tecumseh, with a party of older, experienced warriors, waited in ambush. A strange bird-call from the maple brought the hidden Indians to the ready.

The river men, as brown and tough as any Indian, were coming with a load of cargo intended for delivery to the settlers in the west – bales of cotton, blankets, barrels of

sugar, flour and salt, a quantity of gunpowder, and several chests of tea. This was a magnificent haul for the Indians, quite apart from the fierce fun of fighting and killing white men.

The strange bird called again, and twenty-five rifles cracked out their greeting. The two steersmen were instantly killed and the boats veered helplessly about. The river men reached for their guns and shot into the bushes. But there was no time for a second round. Tecumseh had reached the flat-boat and was flailing about with his tomahawk. The Shawnee swarmed aboard and killed all the passengers and river men but one. This poor wretch was taken ashore from his hiding-place between a cask of tea and a bale of blankets. He was given full Shawnee justice, although his sin was no more than that of having a white skin.

Tecumseh watched the torture and the terrible ultimate

burning at the stake. He, whose belt carried three scalps from the flat-boat, watched, and a fierce revulsion rose within him. When it was over he stood and demanded a hearing. With searing passionate words he proclaimed to his elders that to torture and burn a helpless man, a man with his hands tied in a bag behind his back, was the work of cowards. He attacked the rules of war handed down to the Shawnee for untold years. He scorned the tribal thought trails which no one had ever questioned before. He reviled the chiefs for their actions. He was so fierce and so eloquent in his unprecedented attack upon a cherished Shawnee custom that never again was a prisoner tortured, never again a victim tied to a stake while a fire was lit about it, in Tecumseh's presence. The arrogant youngster, cowardly in his first testing, flaunted his strange independent views to his elders and compelled them to accept them.

There was no real end to the fighting between the Shawnee and Kentucky for many years. As late as 1788, five years after the treaty had been signed among the white men, Blackfish was still raiding in Kentucky.

Blackfish was old now, and rheumatic, but fighting was his life: he must fight still. He went with Tecumseh, Jim Blue Jacket, son of the newly elected war chief of the Shawnee, and Blue Jacket himself on a little raid. The old chief entered the house of a settler, tomahawk in hand. Suddenly the daughter of the house, creeping up behind him, drove a butcher knife up to its hilt in his back. The great fighter, the hero of a hundred raids, died in the most ignominious way open to an Indian. The shameful fact was never revealed. Blackfish was buried secretly and a heroic story of a heroic death proclaimed. No member of the settler's family lived to call it a lie.

The great heroes of Tecumseh's boyhood were all dead now. He had no home, no family ties. For three years he and his brother Cheeseekau wandered with a band of Kickapoo, a Shawnee tribe. They moved down to visit the Shawnee in Illinois on the lower Ohio.

The young braves lounged about the camp a little bored. Early one evening a faint, distant thudding trembled through the earth. The bellow and roar as of a distant herd of angry cows followed the tremor of the earth. They leapt for their ponies. The buffalo were coming! Here was the greatest sport!

On came the great beasts, bellowing and pawing, and on came the Indians in two files, cutting the band into groups as a cowboy cuts his herd. They drove them, encircled, towards a small deep valley, where they fell helpless over the cliff, and could not climb out. Then the braves went in to the kill. As the exhausted herd pounded and scrambled to its extermination, one fat bull, the biggest and most handsome of the lot, slipped out beyond his tormentors and fled to the freedom and safety of the upper plain. Tecumseh urged his tired pony after the big brute. The mare, usually so sure-footed and aware of danger, dropped her foot into a gopher hole and fell heavily, throwing her rider free of her onto a rock. The buffalo galloped to safety over the shoulder of the rise, but Tecumseh lay where he had been thrown. He could not rise then or for many weeks after. His left thigh was broken and he lay in the Shawnee settlement, a visitor and an invalid, for nearly a year while his leg healed. A long, curved scar marked his skin for ever, and the bone, set in the Indian fashion, was never quite straight again. In his buckskins the wound and the defect did not show. When he was stripped for the war dance, the scar puckered white and evil-looking on the copper of his oiled skin. Jealous chiefs, watching, said that he had a leg like a bent bow.

When he was better he could still outrun his braves. As his strength became the strength of a man, he became the acknowledged leader of his Shawnee. He stood out among the tribes his band visited as someone to be remembered, one worthy of being followed. They remembered the strong line of his jaw-bone, the dignity of his bearing, and the words that came to him like flocks of birds. He seemed never to have to search for them.

While Tecumseh lay healing on the lower Ohio the fruitful and lovely valleys of the Scioto and the Miami were being overrun with Americans. Ten thousand settlers a year were travelling into the west. Towns were being established, governments were set up. The shrill demands of the settlers that the Shawnee should be stopped for ever from attacking the Ohio River flat-boats reached the ear of final authority. Harmar, the Commander-in-Chief of the United States Army, was ordered to move into the Indian country and "clean up". With 1,400 men he marched through the Shawnee country, right into the heart of the Miami tribal lands. This was Little Turtle's country, his home and his realm.

Little Turtle, a warrior and strategist of no mean ability, gathered the braves of a dozen tribes and administered a series of stinging defeats. They were as humiliating as they were unexpected. They sent the Commander-in-Chief of the United States Army scuttling back to Fort Washington to resign his commission. But he had left his mark on the land. Five times the Shawnee towns on the Maumee had been left smoking ruins.

Tecumseh came back to his home country on the Ohio to find open warfare between the Indians and the whites, with

Blue Jacket commanding the Shawnee.

The Americans could plainly see that if the Ohio country was to be safe for settlers, the Shawnee, the Delaware, and the Miami would have to be moved out of it. Three American generals tried, the year after Harmar's humiliation, to force the Indians to recognize the purchase of the land. Congress ordered a fort to be built at the headwaters of the Maumee. And if there had to be an army to protect the builders of it, then the Governor and Commander, St. Clair, must recruit an army. Two thousand soldiers marched north towards the new fort. It was the largest force ever seen in the North-west.

The strength, steel, and manpower of two thousand Americans was to be pitted against the Indian alliance of Shawnee, Miami, and Delaware. Blue Jacket depended on Tecumseh for information on the movement of the American army. The young Shawnee was an admirable scout, always invisible himself, seeing all that the enemy did. Blue Jacket laid his plans on Tecumseh's information.

Tecumseh's band were too few in number to attack in their first full-scale engagement. But their eyes were on the enemy, and there were strange occurrences in the camp of the Americans. Odd movements in the bushes, strange noises in the treetops, and weird bird-calls kept the sentries on the alert and the troops from sleeping. A shot into the tree from which the curious animal noises came brought down no game. The troops were apprehensive. Memories of savage Indian assaults, stories of torture tapped on their nerves.

St. Clair went into camp near the headwaters of the Wabash in November. The army, on the march for two months now, had not seen an Indian.

The night was quiet on November 3, 1791 – for the

sentries, the quietest in weeks. Just before sunrise they yawned in their places, ready for the sun to signal their release. Then, with appalling suddenness, with no word of warning, the Indians were there. Hundreds of Indians, screaming, yelling, paint-streaked, and terrifying, leapt upon the Americans.

Blue Jacket of the Shawnee, Buckongahelos of the Delaware, Little Turtle of the Miami split the morning air with the war-cry and fell upon the enemy. Tecumseh was one of the first three warriors to plunge through the American defence. Panic struck the Long Knives like a bolt from the sky.

With the grinning, slashing Indians upon them, the soldiers thought of nothing but escape. They threw away their arms and ammunition and fled for their lives. Six hundred and twenty-nine American regular soldiers were killed and

two hundred and fifty wounded. Many women who had followed the army felt the sudden steel of the tomahawk and closed their eyes for ever. The white man's army was utterly destroyed.

St. Clair's army suffered one of the worst defeats that the Long Knives had ever endured at the hands of either white man or red. Butler, the Major-General, tried again and again in vain to bring his panic-stricken men to order. A whirling tomahawk finished Butler's command, and he lay dead with the others. St. Clair, the Governor and leader, escaped. But his political life, which had been a distinguished one, was over. He resigned his posts and crept away, ashamed and disgraced, into poverty and obscurity.

The Indians were wild with joy, jubilant and boastful. Sheer terror spread through the white man's settlements for hundreds of miles eastward.

Blue Jacket and Little Turtle looked with great approval on Tecumseh, quiet and content, his war club beside him. The young Shawnee had leapt with the first into the glorious fight.

For the next year the Ohio was seldom free from the fearful sound of the Shawnee war-cry. Now on one side of the Ohio, now on the other, Tecumseh led his little band of warriors, raiding and horse-stealing, fearless and free.

One evening after a successful horse-stealing expedition on the Kentucky shore, Tecumseh encountered Simon Kenton again. Scouts from Kenton's party, out looking for the missing animals, came upon Tecumseh and his men, laughing with the fun of stealing the white man's horses. The scouts stole back to Kenton's camp and schemed for the attack on the Indians and the return of the horses. Kenton's party of twenty-two would divide into two parts, each approaching the Indians from the opposite side. There were only ten Indians; they could be easily dispatched and the horses retrieved. So that they might recognize each other in the darkness of the dense woods about the camp, Kenton suggested the countersign "Boone".

Kenton took his party one way, the other leader filed off in the opposite direction, and a boy was sent to herd the horses, grazing now in the river bottoms. Tecumseh lay under a pine tree at the edge of the camp, his war club beside him, "a weapon which he invariably carried in peace and war", Sinnamatha – Stephen Ruddell – said. Kenton's war party rushed upon him. He leapt to his feet, swinging his war club and shouting for Sinnamatha. Big Fish answered from the darkness and raised the Indian cry. Tecumseh heard the call "Boone", and knew that another party could be expected. "Boone!" he shouted, "Boone!"

All the Indians, swarming out of their bark tents, shrieked

"Boone", and there was hopeless confusion in the Kentucky band. Tecumseh flailed about with the great club and killed one man instantly. Kenton in the darkness, with every man singing "Boone", could not distinguish friend from enemy. He fled with his men after him, glad to escape the hornet's nest they had stirred up. U. S. 1322787

Tecumseh took one man prisoner. The man McIntyre had tried to get away with one of the horses and stayed too long about it. Tecumseh left him tied up in the camp while he went to see to the horses. When he returned he found to his white rage that McIntyre had been killed.

The men who killed him never forgot the terrible anger of Tecumseh when he found what they had done. They were miserable wretched cowards, he told them, no better than squaws; a prisoner, a helpless creature, was not to be touched.

They must have puzzled greatly over this strange quirk in Tecumseh's mind. Half an hour before, he had killed a man with his club. How was this different? Stories of Tecumseh's strangeness even as a child came back to them. He had interfered with a man who, out of boredom, perhaps, or slight irritation, was beating his wife, and had thrown him down. He went about his village mending wigwams of the old who had no sons to help them. The tribal customs were not always acceptable to Tecumseh.

Once more, now, Tecumseh turned south, and joined his brother Cheeseekau to lead a fight in the war of the Cherokee against the white. Once more the brothers repeated the pattern of raid and counter-raid, burning, scalping, retreat when the gun-fire became too hot. Fear of the Creek, the Cherokee and the Shawnee drove the settlers into the block-house and stockade at Buchanan Station in Tennessee.

The night before Cheeseekau, with Tecumseh second in command, was to attack the Buchanan Station stronghold,

Cheeseekau felt the premonition of death come upon him. He was to die tomorrow. In the morning he led the assault on the stockade. The Indian fire was too feeble for the stout timbers of the blockhouse. But they fought it out for a while, even in the face of the cannon fire of "Little Swivel", an American artillery piece. Then Cheeseekau, almost as if to court his destiny, climbed the blockhouse roof, and tried to fire it. A shot brought him to the ground. Another shot killed him instantly.

Tecumseh buried his brother in a secret place, unmarked, and swore vengeance on his killers.

The wandering Shawnee formally elected Tecumseh as their leader. The call of their northern home was strong upon them after the defeat at Buchanan Station. But Tecumseh said he would not return until he had the blood of the white men who had killed Cheeseekau.

For a few months the Chickamauga towns felt the force of Shawnee vengeance. Settlers woke to the horror of the Shawnee cry, to the flash of the tomahawk, to the smell of burning. Few men ever escaped Tecumseh's scalping-knife, but no woman or child was ever hurt.

Tecumseh learned much in these weeks. He learned that forts defended by artillery would not be taken by Indian arms. He learned that white men could not stand against the Indian quick thrust and ambush style of fighting. His reputation as a fighter grew among the Indians. Even the whites were compelled to respect him. He felt a bond between him and the Creek, his mother's people. They would be loyal to him if he should need their loyalty.

He was still visiting the Creek when a message came to him from Blue Jacket. Blue Jacket needed the Shawnee warrior at home.

3. The Blacksnake Coils and Strikes

GENERAL "Mad Anthony" Wayne, with terrifying deliberation, prepared for the conquest of the Indian lands in the Ohio valley. The U.S. Army had suffered enough humiliation at the hands of the savages. There was to be no unpreparedness this time, no recurrence of the fates of Harmar and St. Clair. No one knows now why the General was called "Mad Anthony". He worked in a leisurely, thoughtful, well-reasoned way towards his end. To the Indians, in the years after the St. Clair massacre, he became the "Blacksnake", because of the deliberate nature of his operations.

Little Turtle counselled against fighting Wayne. His hot blood had cooled in the Miami fighting and he advised meeting the Blacksnake in peaceful discussion. But the Shawnee would have none of this suggestion. Blue Jacket threw "Coward!" at Little Turtle, and Little Turtle lost command of the Miami. William Wells, one of Little Turtle's adopted white sons, went openly over to Wayne, and became a scout for him. A foster-brother of Tecumseh's was Wells's superior officer. There were friends turned into enemies in the army of the Blacksnake.

Blue Jacket won the command of the allied Indian tribes whose home in and about the Ohio valley the Americans were determined to have. Blue Jacket appointed Tecumseh as head of his scouts. News of every movement of Wayne's army reached Blue Jacket's cabin from Tecumseh and his men.

Wayne was marching north from Cincinnati, Tecumseh reported. He had nearly four thousand men. To make his way safe as he went, he was building forts. Their names were Hamilton, St. Clair, Greenville, Recovery, and Defiance.

It proved possible to attack Wayne's supply train at Fort St. Clair. Fifteen Long Knives were killed in this exercise. Then winter came on and the Blacksnake slept at Greenville. He slept through the spring and into the summer. Would he never wake?

In June three hundred pack-horses loaded with food were preparing to go to Fort Recovery. Ninety riflemen were guarding the convoy. Tecumseh advised and Blue Jacket acted. Wayne's detachment was less than a quarter of a mile on its way when it was attacked. Tecumseh blazed into the enemy with Blue Jacket's eager warriors. Twenty-two white men were killed and thirty wounded. The officers in command lay dead, and the Indians continued to attack the fort

itself for another day before carrying off their own dead.

These small successes whetted the Indian appetite for battle.

In August the strain of long waiting and watching began to tell on the warriors. They were spoiling for a fight. Even Blue Jacket, experienced and wary enough, was anxious now to meet the Blacksnake in open combat. How could he fight him, when he slept in the fort at Greenville? Part of the Indian strategy was to avoid attacking stockaded forts. They had learned that wisdom at Buchanan Station.

In August 1794 Tecumseh gave a sign. The Blacksnake stirred at last. He was moving down the left bank of the Maumee and he led a prodigious army of fighters. At least three thousand men in Wayne's forces marched against the allied tribes. They were tough, thoroughly trained, experienced fighters. Dragoons, mounted on the best of Kentucky's bluegrass-bred horses, proudly rode along. Gun-carriages brought artillery to face the Indians, steel wheels rattling over the corduroy, well-trained gunners following. These

were the men who knew how to use the big guns, and were itching for a chance, after lying quietly all winter. A thousand fixed bayonets gleamed along the banks of the Maumee, ready to find a home in Indian flesh. And at the head of them all – Anthony Wayne, the Blacksnake himself. He was greatly experienced, had fought the best troops that England had sent to America, and now was irrevocably determined.

Tecumseh's spies reported, and the chiefs of the Shawnee, the Miami, the Delaware, and all the allied tribes held a great Council Fire. Little Turtle, deposed and suspected of sympathy with the Americans, counselled further waiting. He was voted down. Tomorrow the Blacksnake would know the force of Shawnee hate. Tonight they would dance their terrible tribal war dance.

The dark forest rang with the staccato, piercing, hooting cries of the braves. The earth shook to the pounding of their rhythmic leapings, and in the light of the fire their painted faces gleamed. Feinting and thrusting, they whirled imaginary tomahawks in the dusk, foretelling the action of tomorrow. The Shawnee crouched, then leapt. In a frightful masquerade they hurled themselves upon a startled enemy, scalped, and yelled in victory. They ceremonially scattered tobacco and sumac on the dance-ground, to keep off the evil spirits who might conspire to their undoing.

Blue Jacket had half as many warriors as Wayne. The Indians had small arms only, no artillery. There were no bayonets in Indian hands. Their training was all for fighting in the bush – the sudden assault, the surprise attack, the rush in and the rush out, the bloody mission accomplished. Now they would face a body of relentless fighters, armed with steel.

Blue Jacket's warriors took up their stand directly in the

path of the oncoming American army, along the west bank of the Maumee. Just a mile or two away, British soldiers were garrisoned at Fort Miami. There was no stir in the British fort.

A tornado, crashing through Ohio a few days before, had ripped up great trees and piled the uprooted giants in a natural abatis. From behind the fallen timbers the Indians fought their desperate battle.

Tecumseh's scouts shot into Wayne's advance guard. Blue Jacket's men fired into the oncoming Long Knives. But now the Blacksnake struck, and struck again. His sharp-shooting riflemen sniped off any Indian head that dared to show above the abatis. The great guns roared and shells burst over the barricade. Horsemen dashed towards the Indian warriors and Wayne ordered a bayonet charge, the most awful of all to the Indian mind.

It was too much for the red men. Many of Blue Jacket's braves turned and ran. Three times Tecumseh led his band of Shawnee back to fight again when they, in terror of the flashing steel and crash of guns, had thought retreat the only possibility. Tecumseh's elder brother, Sauwaseekau, fell dead. Tecumseh's gun jammed. He threw it away and called for a gun. Someone handed him a fowling-piece, suitable for bringing down ducks.

Fowling-piece to cannon – this was the might of the red man to the white.

And now the terrible bayonets came on. There was no end to the line of American troops. Blue Jacket's men fled.

As a last cocky gesture, Tecumseh and three of his friends charged a group of Americans guarding a gun. The Indians drove off the gunners, cut the horses' traces, and rode into retreat on American mounts.

Fully conscious of the action at Fallen Timbers, almost within sight of it, the British soldiers at Fort Miami offered no help. When the battle was over, the Indians in full retreat clamoured at the gates of the fort, seeking shelter and asylum. The gates were barred against them. The commander said, "You are too painted, my children." He kept them out.

Tecumseh never forgot the rejection and the insult.

The Indians could not understand the situation. Jay's Treaty, signed in the same year, had declared that the British fur-trading posts were on American ground, as the peace of 1783 had drawn the line, and that they must be given up. The Indians knew that the British bitterly resented the line.

But they could not see that the British must be neutral.

The American opinion was that the British were definitely encouraging the Indians to warfare. They believed that British guns and ammunition were being generously distributed to the Indians. All sorts of extravagant tales came out of this belief, although it would seem only common sense to realize that fur-trading was the great business of the British in North America, and that Indians on the war-path bring in no furs. William Henry Harrison, one of Wayne's young aides, insisted that Englishmen painted like Shawnee warriors were fighting side by side with the Indians.

The defeat at Fallen Timbers was decisive and complete. Wayne marched on through a score of Indian villages and razed them. Yet again the cornfields, the gardens, and the storehouses turned into smoke and ashes. Wayne left no doubt in any Indian mind that he was master now. He was king in the lands they had thought were their own.

In the 1783 treaty, the British had failed to provide for the Indians. They had ceded land to the United States that was not theirs to cede. The case of the occupying Indians was not considered. Almost immediately after the signing of the treaty the British regretted their omission and tried to persuade the Americans to create an Indian state, inside the American border. Nothing came of this idea. All the white men, British and American alike, had failed the Indians.

The defeated warriors retired to winter quarters and considered their hopeless state. By spring they were ready to listen to peace overtures from Wayne. All, or nearly all, the chiefs and fighting braves were ready to accept what they could get by a treaty.

But not Tecumseh.

The victorious Blacksnake offered peace at a price. He invited the defeated chiefs and warriors to a great peace meeting at Greenville. Bitter, resentful, and forced to be reconciled, a thousand warriors and nearly a hundred chiefs, and their squaws, moved in the leisurely Indian fashion upon Greenville. They set up their camp there and for nearly two months the parley continued.

Wayne offered the Indians twenty thousand dollars and annuities amounting to nine and a half thousand dollars for twenty-five thousand square miles of land. The Greenville Treaty line struck across central Ohio far north of the beautiful river. It ran from Fort Recovery to the Cuyahoga River. South, it went from Fort Recovery on the Ohio River to the mouth of the Kentucky. Within this huge square of land the home-sites of the Shawnee had stood. All was now to belong to the Americans. Among the special grants was a large plot of land to George Rogers Clark, who had several times burned the Shawnee villages.

Blue Jacket signed the treaty for the Shawnee. His despair must have been deep as he saw the homeland of his tribe pass into white hands – and his the hand that had signed it away. Perhaps a little of the Turtle's conviction and apprehension came to the Shawnee war chief, and he saw that his people could never defeat the whites. He must get what he could for them. Little Turtle, by craft, got for the Miami twice what the other tribes were promised.

Twelve tribes signed the mischievous, tragic papers; allied tribes with names like Indian music shared equally in the treaty money. They were Wyandot, Shawnee, Delaware, Ottawa, Chippewa, Potawatomi, Kickapoo, Kaskaskia, Wea, and Piankeshaw.

It took two days for the writing of the treaty. Twelve copies had to be made and signed, with appropriate ceremony by all. There was feasting and drinking while the papers were being made ready. Perhaps when the moment came to sign away their hunting-grounds, to agree to give up all white prisoners, and never more to protest the encroachment of the white men in the valley of the Ohio, the chiefs, having eaten and drunk their fill, did not care any more.

They held out their hands for the money, and in time received at least some of it. At Greenville the Blacksnake turned into "Wabang", which means "tomorrow".

So it was done and the land was gone; pride, self-respect, and honour went with it. Chiefs whose names had struck terror all along the Kentucky border were set on the treaty paper. Blue Jacket, Little Turtle, New Corn, Leatherlips, Red Pole, Black Hoof – all had made their mark. There was no mark for Tecumseh. He had defiantly refused to go to Greenville.

Tecumseh never accepted the Greenville Treaty in principle, but he could do nothing but accept it in fact. The white idea of the ownership of land was foreign to the Indian mind. Tecumseh thought long about the treaty. During the years between the signing of the Greenville pact and the establishment of the Indiana Territory in 1800, the idea of joint Indian ownership of all Indian lands crystallized in Tecumseh's brain. It seemed to him that by the treaty of Greenville, when twelve tribes received equal shares for the sale of a huge block of land, the government of the Americans had admitted that the right to the lands belonged to *all* the Indians. It should not be possible to buy a piece of land from one tribe without the consent of all the tribes. The purchase money should be shared by all.

These were thoughtful years for Tecumseh, as he grew to full maturity. He began to be accepted by the tribes, not as just a Shawnee chieftain, but as the Chief of the Ohio.

As a boy, Tecumseh was always an effective speaker, able to persuade his friends. The Shawnee produced great orators, and appreciated the power of dramatic speech. Tecumseh became one of the greatest of Indian orators, following in the tradition of Cornstalk.

Oratory was theatre, literature, and art to the Indian. The Shawnee drew on nature, the rivers, the waterfalls, the clouds, and the animals of sky and forest for their imagery. Men who came to hear Tecumseh speak, whether white men or Indians, never forgot the eloquence and force of his delivery.

After Greenville, Blue Jacket himself did honour to Tecumseh and paid him a visit. He tried to make Tecumseh see that the Greenville pact was unavoidable. But Tecumseh shook his head, and his way parted from Blue Jacket's way. He removed his band of Shawnee from the tribal organization and set off on his own.

They wandered beyond the treaty land, now here, now there. They settled on the Great Miami, and put in a crop of corn. When it was harvested they moved again, always searching restlessly for a land to take the place of the lovely Ohio country, where now the white man, unmolested, ploughed his fields and raised his crop. The Shawnee were fierce and war-loving, but they were an honourable people. No Shawnee broke his word. The white settlers in the Shawnee country were safe.

The Delaware on the White River invited Tecumseh and his band to live near them. In war-time it would be good to have this brilliant chief with his ever-growing band of warriors close at hand. Tecumseh accepted their invitation and settled his people just west of the Greenville line.

The reputation of Tecumseh was growing fast. The good-looking boy had turned into "one of the finest-looking men I have ever seen", as an American army officer said. Exceptional intelligence glowed in his unusual eyes, hazel-coloured, deep-set, and abnormally quick to observe. These were strange eyes in an Indian face. Could it be that somewhere in the background of the generations there had been a drop of white blood? His skin was pale copper, not the mahogany colour of many of his braves. His foster-brothers said that he had unusually strong, even, white teeth, and his flash of a smile was as frequent as the terrible frown that could reduce a brave to terror.

By white standards Tecumseh was not a tall man – five feet nine in his moccasins. He was very erect of carriage, slight in build, with powerful chest and shoulders. He was phenomenally quick in his movements, phenomenally successful as a hunter. In a hunting contest for deerskins while his band was resting on Buck Creek, after Greenville, the young men separated to bring down their deer. Three days were allowed for the testing of their skills. The average bag was three skins. One skilful hunter brought in twelve. Tecumseh laid down thirty.

Tecumseh's mentality was as far above the average warrior's as was his hunting skill. There was no written Shawnee, but on the clear sheet of his mind no word was ever erased. The Greenville Treaty in all its complexity of clauses was only one of the many that Tecumseh knew by heart.

Tecumseh had little regard for possessions. A mighty hunter, he gave away meat and skins to those who he considered needed them more than he did. He knew he could get what he needed at any time. He was an intellectual, more interested in ideas than in material possessions.

The overruling passion of his life, as he led and expanded his band of warriors, was his hatred of the whites. "When I look on a white face, it makes my flesh creep."

Perhaps he protested too much.

Tecumseh was twenty-eight and as yet unmarried. It was most unusual for a chief to remain unmarried. As he walked by the tents of the young women, black eyes followed that straight, quick figure. He might have had his choice.

Suddenly he married. He married a woman who was so unattractive, bad-tempered, and ugly, and so much older than he, that he might almost have married to spite his warriors, who perhaps teased him about having no wife. It was as if to say, "Very well, if I must marry, here is my wife." Her name was Manete; and she was half white!

Manete bore Tecumseh a child, a son. The little boy was a light-skinned child. His father showed little interest in him. He who was so quick to see and forcibly object to the maltreatment of women by their husbands treated his own with contempt. It was not in his nature to beat her, but he gave her scant consideration.

Tecumseh asked his wife to make a pouch for his war paint. He found the materials and gave them to her. She said that she could not sew, but that she would find someone who could. His temper flared. He told her to trouble herself no more, but to leave his house. He gave her an armful of presents and sent her away. She was permitted to set herself up with the little boy and she brought him up until he was eight. Then Tecumseh took him to his sister Tecumapease, who had been more of a mother to him than Methoataske had ever been.

Then Tecumseh, who had apparently never been in love, fell violently, deeply, and eternally in love with a pure white woman.

Her name was Rebecca Galloway. She lived on a farm very near Old Chillicothe, where Tecumseh had lived with Blackfish. She was exceptionally blond.

The harsh life of the families who cleared the forest and broke new ground aged the women very early. Their skins were quickly browned leather-like by the sun and roughened by the wind. Settler women in a few seasons looked as weather-beaten as the Indians themselves. They were often as tough.

Rebecca, the young daughter of the settler James Gal-

loway, once in the service of George Rogers Clark, destroyer
of the Shawnee villages, stood out from the rough women of
the settlement like an Easter lily in a field of sunflowers.

Tecumseh stepped quietly into the settler's kitchen one
day, as he had many times before when coming to trade.
There she stood. The chief could say nothing. The fragile
air, the candid, pure face with its wide-set, Irish blue eyes,
caught at his heart.

She was gentle, unafraid, laughing and friendly. Tecumseh forgot that Rebecca belonged to the hated white race
which he was sworn to exterminate. There was nothing of
the white man's insolence, his hauteur, his deceit, in this
frank and lovely creature. The chief of the Ohio, the man
to whom the tribes now looked for salvation from the encroachment of the white man, was able to dissociate Rebecca
Galloway completely in his mind from all the other pale-
faces in the world. As the dazzled moth flickers to the
destructive flame of the candle, Tecumseh came to Rebecca.
He came to look and to marvel, and he came again and again.
His visits in the beginning were very nearly silent, because
he knew only broken, trader, pioneer English, and she knew
no Shawnee at all. Yet she introduced him to a new world.

By ox-cart over the mountains, by flat-boat down the
Ohio, packed in with the guns, the wheat, and the salt, James
Galloway had carried a library of three hundred books. On
one of the early, silent visits, Rebecca put a book into
Tecumseh's lean and powerful hands. He looked, marvelling
at all the evenly squared-off sheets. They were thinner than
the finest birch bark, marked with rows of tiny, neat, black
marks. Some mysterious agent held them very tightly together at one side, and hard, mottled skins covered the white
sheets.

Rebecca took the toy from him and began to read. He listened just to hear her voice. Here and there a word came clear to him out of the music of her tongue. The reader glanced at the chief and saw that he did not understand. She determined to teach this bold and handsome man the meaning of English words.

Tecumseh learned very fast. What he heard from Rebecca after she had vastly enlarged his speaking vocabulary was very different from anything he had ever heard before. She read the story of Alexander the Great to him. The tale laid hold on his heart and mind. He never forgot Alexander, and talked of him, his exploits, and his death until the end of his own life. She read to him from the Bible. "The Lord caused the sea to go back by a strong east wind all that night, and made the sea dry land, and the waters were divided, and the children of Israel went into the midst of the sea upon the dry ground; and the waters were a wall unto them on their right hand and on their left."

A Shawnee could understand a reading like that. For when the Master of Life set the Shawnee on this great island, which the white-skinned people were taking from them, it was that way, too. The Great Spirit had parted the waters and laid dry the floor of the sea, so that the Shawnee could come in.

The idyll of Rebecca and Tecumseh went on for many, many months. The chief brought her a tortoise-shell comb for her beautiful hair, and the tenderest meat, the softest furs from his hunting. His most skilful boat-builders made an elaborately decorated birch-bark canoe for her. The two floated down the Miami together, able to talk and sing together now. Tecumseh called the girl "Star of the Lake". He asked James Galloway if he might marry his daughter.

The settler saw advantages in the match. No other young man in the pioneer community could stand beside this Indian chief in brains or prospects.

"Ask the girl," he said.

Tecumseh dressed himself in a fine new buckskin suit, made from the skin of young deer, soft and supple as velvet. He carried in his hand as a present "fifty broaches of silver". He paddled her out beyond the shadows of a fringe of trees, on the Miami.

The proud man, humble before this young girl, put his question. She was flattered, of course. Tecumseh was a name to conjure with in these settlements. She said, in the English words she had taught him to understand, "I will marry you, Tecumseh." She saw the gleam in the eyes, the sudden grasp of the paddle. "But I could not be an Indian wife!" She lifted her small white hands, moth-like in the dusk. "I could not do as Indian women do, fetch the firewood, work the skins. Come away from the tribes, and live as we do here. Wear the clothes my father wears. We could be happy that way, Tecumseh!"

The canoe came in to shore, and Tecumseh lifted the girl onto the land. "In another moon," he said, "I will come again, and bring my answer."

He was gone, a cruel decision awaiting him.

When the new moon was low in the western sky, Tecumseh came again to the Galloway farm. He was an Indian. No amount of changing clothes or outer habits would make him into a white man. He had sworn undying enmity to the white-skinned race. He was a chief, an Indian chief. His people looked to him; he could not in honour desert them. He went silently back through the forest, carrying his people's trust, unbroken with him. He never saw Rebecca again.

For seven years, until 1805, Tecumseh and his ever-growing band of devoted Shawnee lived on the White River, neighbours to the Delaware. Tecumseh hunted, had his crops put in and harvested, and with his small, selected group of warriors travelled very extensively. He rode all over the Wabash valley and south to the Shawnee settlement in Missouri. Sometimes he thought he might take his band and cross the vast Mississippi, and live there, far beyond where the white man spread his problems. But he knew when he consulted his heart and his conscience that he could not forsake the Shawnee.

The white men were coming in thousands. Rumours that there would be a new North-west Territory reached the Indians. Ohio was said to be reaching statehood soon. Farmers from poor land in the east were pushing west to find better. The fertile valleys of the Ohio were filling up with old soldiers on land grants. Plans for cities were made, and men speculating in Ohio land made fortunes. Ohio was becoming a white man's world, bewildering and terrifying. But the peace was kept between the red man and the white.

Since Greenville there had never been a general tribal conference. In 1799 a great council was called, to convene in a grove a few miles north of Urbana. White men and Indians gathered in the woods to settle, if possible, growing suspicious of broken treaty, and to gain assurance that all was well, and would be well, between the white men and the red.

Long, dramatic, flowery speeches were the main feature of the meeting. Spokesmen for the white men gave of their best at Urbana, explaining their works and their needs. Old sachems from the tribes spoke with greater drama, calling upon the rich imagery of poetic Indian utterance to give power to their words. Dechouset, a Frenchman brought up with Shawnee, was chief interpreter.

Until Tecumseh rose to speak, Dechouset was at home in his work. He faithfully reported what the Indians had said. But Tecumseh's speech utterly defeated the interpreter. It was so forceful, so eloquent, calling upon such vivid and elaborate figures of speech, one following so fast upon the other, that Dechouset could but sit like the others, amazed and motionless. White men understanding no word of Shawnee were aroused to applause by the fiery declamation, the power of the rich voice. Here spoke the voice of the Shawnee.

Every speech that Tecumseh made lived in the minds of his people. In the eyes of both the white and the red races, he was inspired. He never lied, so that all men believed him. He was fair-minded and humane, so that all men trusted him. He was wise, and gaining in wisdom, so that people in trouble came to him for advice. In many cases of acute trouble between Indian and white, he represented the Indians in the court of the white.

A farmer named Thomas Herrod living about sixteen miles from Chillicothe was murdered. All the marks of Indian killing were found upon him. He had been shot, tomahawked, and scalped while working in his own fields. A few days later old chief Wawillaway of the Shawnee was murdered. Was this retaliation?

The situation was dangerous. Until now the peace of Greenville had not been broken. Here was tinder to the hand of both red and white. Farmers and their families quailed in terror at the thought of Indians again on the war-path, visiting their rage on the scattered farmhouses. Many of them crowded into Chillicothe, seeking the safety of the town.

The Indians in their turn fled westward, fearful of war with the whites. It looked for a few weeks as if the newly-born state of Ohio might be christened in blood.

What were the Indians doing out in the west? Were they plotting a full-scale breaking of the treaty? Were the whites gathering soldiers to fight and punish the whole red race for the murder of one man?

A group of very brave white men mounted their horses and rode into the Indian country in search of Tecumseh. They travelled all the way from Chillicothe to the White River to find him. Neither he nor any of his Shawnee band had heard of the murder of Herrod or the death of the old Shawnee chief. The white men asked Tecumseh to go back with them to Chillicothe, and to give his assurance that the Indian tribes were not planning an uprising against the whites.

The image of Cornstalk rose very vividly before Tecumseh. He had gone to the camp of the white men at their request, and seven bullets in his body had been his quick reward. The chief looked at the spokesman. Could he be trusted? Could he, Tecumseh, take the risk of going, without his warriors, into the white man's country to plead for his Indians? For a day he considered, and then consented. He could not refuse a chance to further the interests of his people.

He mounted his horse, and without escort rode back with the party of whites to plead the Indian cause before a crowd of hostile white men. He was very silent on the journey, planning his speech as he went. If he should live long enough to give it, the plan and the words were to be ready.

It was a rough crowd that Tecumseh faced. Tough pioneer farmers, complete with rifles and whisky jugs, buckskin shirts, and buckskin leggings tied about the knees for protection from rattlesnakes, stared at the Shawnee. This Indian was going to have to do some fast talking to clear his race. They fingered their rifles.

The first governer of the new state convened the meeting. He maintained order with a firm hand. The interpreter was Stephen Ruddell, Tecumseh's foster-brother, the Sinnamatha of his young days. It must have been some support to the chief to see Big Fish here. The Governor introduced Tecumseh and he rose to present the case for the Indians.

He stepped confidently to the speaker's place, and for a long moment looked out over his audience, the rough men of the frontier. He felt power rise within him. He could bring this audience to him if he chose his words well. As usual, he started to speak in a casual, drifting, almost conversational tone, rising as he caught the men's full attention to bursts of flaming eloquence. A member of his audience said afterwards:

"When Tecumseh rose to speak, as he cast his eye over the vast multitude . . . he appeared one of the most dignified men I ever beheld. While this orator of nature was speaking, the crowd preserved the most profound silence. From the confident manner in which he spoke of the intention of the Indians to adhere to the treaty of Greenville, and live in peace and friendship with their white brethren, he dispelled, as if by magic, the apprehensions of the whites . . . the settlers returned to their deserted farms, and business generally was resumed throughout that region."

Peace descended once more on the Ohio, a peace created by a man who had never held that the Greenville Treaty was just or good, but whose chief had signed it.

4. *"Dark and Bloody Councils"*

OLD CHANGE OF FEATHERS, the Shawnee official prophet, died. Laulewasika, Tecumseh's young brother, snatched at his mantle and became the most astounding prophet that the Shawnee ever possessed.

Laulewasika (Loud Mouth), the big, bad-tempered baby deserted by his mother, grew up to be a loafer. He was too fat to be a hunter, too lazy and too fond of the whisky keg to bestir himself in any way. Like many Indians, he felt in touch with the magic in nature and had some success in healing by magic incantation and the application of herbs. He had lost one eye while he was still a boy. An arrow he was making had split, and shot into his eye. He covered the empty eye-socket with a black handkerchief and walked about, a raffish figure. He followed the whisky from village to village, carrying his small magic with him. Until he was nearly thirty, Loud Mouth was indolent, cadging, gluttonous, and drunken.

White men and Indians alike in Laulewasika's time consumed vast quantities of liquor. The pioneers drank whisky to keep out the cold, and gave it to friends when they helped them build their houses and their forts, but they were not usually drunkards. But an Indian who drank the white man's firewater usually became a confirmed drunkard.

William Henry Harrison was now governor of the newly

organized Indiana territory. And although his chief and strongest aim in life was to grasp the Indians' land, even Harrison felt pity at the sight of "those unhappy people" who were victims of alcohol. They were "half naked, filthy and enfeebled".

A tremendous religious revival, far-reaching and intense, swept through the frontier. Settlers, Indians, dwellers in towns and in forests felt the heightening of the spirit that accompanies the moments in the history of man when he feels that he has come near his God, who hears him cry out. His faith is "revived" and the bond between him and his creator is strengthened.

The members of one group of "revivalists", whites, were called "Shakers". When the ecstasy of communion with their God came upon them, they trembled and shook. In their meetings, when the spirit touched them, they broke into a kind of jerky dance. This was the kind of worship the Indians could understand. They were ceremonial dancers, too.

The Shakers drew Loud Mouth into their ecstasies, although he could not have understood much of what they said. A profound sense of sin came upon the Indian. He slept, and the Master of Life sent him heavy, terrible, and symbolic dreams. He was shown whisky-drinkers being forced to drink hot, molten lead; again and again, they were given the potion. This was to be the fate in the after-life of people who, like himself, rotted their bodies with firewater. This message he was to give to the tribes.

The man of dubious magic was completely transformed. His habits changed utterly. He abandoned his greed and now ate very little. He never again took a drink of whisky. He believed that the Master of Life had given him the task of saving his people. He went about from tribe to tribe, telling them of the code of living that the Master had given him. From time to time the code was changed, added to, and given new illustration by the revelations that were sent to the Prophet in his trances. It began as the Shaker code – to refrain from war, from bloodshed, from all forms of violence; to be just, to pay one's debts, to be kind, and to tell the truth. No liquor was ever to be drunk, and inter-tribal war was forbidden. The ban on war between the tribes was the most astonishing rule of all.

Loud Mouth changed his name to Tenskwautawau, which means "The Open Door". The self-proclaimed prophet was to be the open door by whose teaching the Indians should enter a happier, holier life. He was amazingly successful in his converts. Gradually not only the Shawnee, but hundreds of Indians from the other tribes, flocked to the Prophet's camp.

In 1805, the Master of Life commanded Tenskwautawau to go "to the big ford where the peace was made", and to found a centre of worship there. He went to Greenville with his many followers, and built a very large tabernacle. Fifty or sixty dwellings of the Prophet's followers rose about the tabernacle.

A call went out from the older Shawnee chiefs at the Glaize River for a gathering of the tribe there. Black Hoof, the white man's friend up at the Glaize, waited in vain for them. The Shawnee, moving up towards the Glaize, went no farther than Greenville. Greenville became Shawnee headquarters. Delaware, Wyandot, Seneca, and Indians from many tribes joined with the Shawnee and the Prophet there.

The Prophet ranged out from Greenville into Indiana,

and, as his disciples increased, so too did his vanity and love
of power. He could not bear that there should still be any
prophet but himself in the Indian country, any other magic
worker. Whoever could be accused, rightly or wrongly, of
witchcraft must be put to death. No proof was needed but
the pointing of the Prophet's finger at the wretched victim.

Among the Delaware, already a martyred tribe for their
acceptance of the Christians' religion, the Prophet found
signs of witchcraft. An ancient grandmother, suspected of
keeping a "medicine bag", was slowly roasted in fire on the
Prophet's orders, to make her confess the whereabouts of the
magic bag. In her death agony, she admitted that she had
such a bag, but said she had given it to her grandson. The
boy was found. He had, he said, once had the bag, and with
the magic from it had flown between twilight and dark all
over Kentucky to the banks of the Mississippi, and back to
the Delaware camp in Indiana.

The Indians refused to put the boy to death. It might be
very dangerous to interfere with such a person. He was set
free to fly again. But the old chief of the Delaware, Teteboxi,
was tortured and burnt. The Prophet had looked into his
eyes, and found evil. Many old Delaware chiefs were killed
on the Prophet's orders.

Tecumseh, coming to Greenville, visited Shawnee and
Delaware camps where the inhabitants were paralysed with
fear. Scores of their people had been killed. The accusation
against them was that they had been disguised as animals,
foxes, weasels, owls.

The chief hurried to his brother, who was full of vanity
and conceit. He told Tecumseh that he had felt hostility in
the camp, especially among the chiefs and sachems. Tonight,
a great feast would be held, and when the chiefs were merry

and full of meat the Prophet's men would fall upon them with their tomahawks, and the evil would be finished. Tecumseh listened in astonishment, stony-faced. He lifted his tomahawk and the Prophet, black robe flowing and raven-wing head-dress askew, lumbered into the forest.

Tecumseh gathered his young chiefs about him, his warriors and braves. He said no blood must flow in the Shawnee tribe, but the power must soon be in the hands of the warriors, since, if the Indians were to have their own country to live in, war would be the only way to secure it.

The Prophet had spoken of the truth that every Shawnee knew – that they sprang from the brain of the Master of Life. When the Shawnee became sinful, the Master took away their knowledge and gave it to the white people. Now the Master was ready to restore all knowledge to the Shawnee; they were to trample the Americans under foot. The moment was upon them.

The old chiefs felt their power slipping from them; the management and direction of the tribes was more and more in the hands of the young men. Tecumseh considered the Prophet's influence, and saw that, properly guided, it might be useful in bringing unity to the tribes. For Tecumseh had conceived a majestic plan. All the Indians would unite in a great confederacy, with one single aim among them. Working and fighting together, they would save their land from the encroachment of the white men.

Harrison learned of the Indian gathering at Greenville, and was displeased. He hated the news of any Indian tribal activity. The Governor sat in his lovely new house in Vincennes and wished he had the power of the Roman generals. His knowledge of the Romans was great – his reading was constantly of those far-off, great warriors.

When news of the Prophet and his magic and his dangerous power over the Indians came to Harrison, in April 1806, he sent a message to the Delaware.

"My children . . . who is this pretended Prophet who dares to speak in the name of the Great Creator? Examine him. Is he more wise or virtuous than you are yourselves? . . . Demand of him some proofs. . . . If God has really employed him, He has, doubtless, authorized him to perform some miracles. . . . Ask him to cause the sun to stand still – the moon to alter its course – the rivers to cease to flow. . . . If he does these things, you may then believe that he has been sent from God."

Long in advance, astronomers knew that an eclipse of the sun was coming, but Harrison did not. On June 16 the sky would darken at midday. Men of science and government officials had set up observation stations well ahead of the day.

The Prophet learned early of the phenomenon. He told his followers that on the sixteenth day of the next moon, he could cause the sun to cover her face. If Harrison wanted a miracle, the Prophet could oblige, and on a grand scale.

A huge crowd of Indians gathered at Greenville about the Prophet's wigwam. An hour before the sky would darken, he stepped out before them, a commanding and sinister one-eyed figure. He was a strong and heavy man, and he wore a tall and spreading crest of raven's wings. A black, flowing robe, as always, clothed him. He stood speechless before the silent people. Then, as the moment drew near, he raised his arm to the sun, drew a circle about it in the air, and muttered a few unintelligible words. Slowly the disc of the moon began to pass before the face of the sun. Birds twittered their night songs in the trees. A strange, unearthly light replaced the light of the sun.

Then the Prophet raised his arms in supplication to the Master of Life. He implored Him, for His red children's sake, to take His hand from the face of the sun and bring light to the island again.

The Indians gazed awe-struck at the manifestation. Would the light come back? Would the Master of Life hear, and draw back the shadow of His hand?

Slowly the disc passed over, and the Prophet's work was done. The story of this greatest of miracles swept the Indian country like a prairie fire. The Prophet himself came almost to believe that he had shrouded the sun by his own magic. No story was now too absurd or too magnificent to be believed. The Prophet could point to a spot on the earth, and instantly a pumpkin as big as a wigwam would be there. He could circle his finger about an ear of corn and twelve men could feed from it. He could, if the Indians would believe him, ask the Master of Life to send down hail, each stone as big as a mortar for grinding corn. The stones would fall on the white men, and the land be left for ever to the Indians.

Harrison, at Vincennes on the Wabash, fidgeted with apprehension at the news of the Prophet's successes. He could think no good of any Indian movement. He was sure that they were being encouraged in villainy by British agents. William Wells, who had defected to the Americans at Fallen Timbers, put Harrison into a state of nervous agitation about the Prophet's operations. Little Turtle, now gone over completely to the whites, and living comfortably on an annuity, encouraged Wells. Together they kept the Governor on tenterhooks.

Greenville became the centre of Harrison's attention. It was in Ohio, well out of his jurisdiction, but it fretted him constantly. Portents of disaster from the Prophet's camp flew about his head like bats. A few pilgrims to the Prophet's religious council always became an "armed force" as reported to Harrison by William Wells. And in Harrison's mind there was no doubt that the arms were British, and that the British were behind every sinister Indian movement.

Harrison's agitation about Greenville as an ammunition dump communicated itself to the Governor of Ohio. A delegation of white men of intelligence and honesty sent by the Governor, called on the Indians in the Prophet's capital to ask why the Prophet's people were in Greenville.

Tecumseh called a great council when the white men arrived. Worthington and McArthur, the leaders of the American group, presented a friendly letter from the Governor of Ohio. Stephen Ruddell translated it into Shawnee, Potawatomi, and Chippewa. McArthur spoke of the friendship between the Americans and their red neighbours, which must continue to exist. He asked why so many Indians, from so far away, had gathered in Greenville. Advice against forming friendships with the British was urgently presented. Blue Jacket, after a night of consideration, answered the Americans. He spoke of a council, held a few days before. This is what was said, as Blue Jacket reported it.

"We see that there is likely to be war between the British and our white brethren, the Americans. Let us unite and consider the sufferings we have undergone, from interfering in the wars of the British. They have often promised to help us, and at last, when we could not withstand the army that came against us and went to the British fort for refuge, the British told us, 'I cannot let you in; you are painted too much, my children.' It was then we saw that the British dealt treacherously with us. We now see them going to war again. Let us not, my brethren, interfere."

Blue Jacket spoke directly to the commissioners. "These, brethren, are the sentiments of all the men who sit around you. It is not that they are afraid of their white brethren, but that they desire peace and harmony. . . ."

The delegation was entirely convinced of the peaceful intentions of the Prophet and his adherents in Greenville.

Tecumseh, Blue Jacket, Chief Roundhead, and Chief Panther travelled back to Chillicothe and met the Governor in conference. At a general council there, Tecumseh gave an impassioned, three-hour speech, in which he reviewed all the Ohio land treaties, and denounced them, every one, as invalid. He included the Greenville Treaty, while Blue Jacket sat beside him. There was no legal ownership of lands north and west of the Ohio. The treaties, so-called, had been made between people who had no right to make them, who did not own the land. He spoke with utter fearlessness and said in burning tones that he would resist any further intention of the whites to encroach on Indian lands. But at the same time he convinced the Governor and his advisers that he did not intend war. The militia, which had been called up largely on account of Harrison's fear, were sent home.

The Governor of Ohio was convinced, but Harrison was not. Fear of the British bothered him again, and in 1807 he sent a stirring speech to the chiefs of the Shawnee.

"My children, listen to me, I speak in the name of your father, the great chief of the Seventeen Fires. It is now twelve years since the tomahawk which you had raised by the advice of your father, the king of Great Britain, was buried in the presence of that great warrior General Wayne, at Greenville.

"My children, you then promised that you would live in peace and friendship with your brothers, the Americans, to acknowledge no other father than the chief of the Seventeen Fires, and never to listen to the proposition of any foreign nations. Have you done so? Have you not always had your ears open to receive bad news from beyond the lakes? . . . My children, shut your ears . . . I have heard black news. The sacred spot where the great council fire was kindled, around which the Seventeen Fires and ten tribes of their children smoked the pipe of peace – that very spot where the Great Spirit heard his red and white children encircle themselves with the chain of friendship, that place has been selected for dark and bloody councils. This business must be stopped. You have called in a number of men from the most distant tribes to listen to a fool, who speaks not the words of the Great Spirit but those of the devil and of the British agents. Let him go to the lakes; he can hear the British more distinctly."

The Prophet provided Harrison's interpreter with an answer of truth and dignity. "Tell my father," he said, "that I wish he would not listen to the bad birds any more. It is the least of our ideas to make any disturbance. I have never been to the British. The Indians came here to hear the words of the Great Spirit."

There was fear of war, and conviction that war would come, between the British and the Americans, but there was not yet war. The bonfire was laid – only the match was needed to light it.

5. Tecumseh Rides the Grand Circuit

TECUMSEH sent the Prophet to Fort Malden, the British fort at Amherstburg on the Detroit River, to see if he could learn when war was to be expected. The redcoats treated him and his Indians kindly, and gave them presents but no information.

Tecumseh came to a great decision. He would move the Prophet and his people from Greenville. It had become a substantial town now, after three years of planning and construction. But it would no longer serve. White settlements were crowding up to it. The people thronging to the Greenville mission were already in need of more food than the area could provide for them. And Harrison had his spies in every corner.

In 1808, Tecumseh directed the Prophet to move the settlement to a tract of land that the Potawatomi and Kickapoo offered. The Miami and Delaware, invited to come and join him there, informed him that it was their land and he could not have it. Tecumseh replied that all the land was owned by the Indians in common. It was not theirs to give or to keep.

The tract, an old Indian habitation, lay on the west bank of the Tippecanoe River, and stretched to the place where the Wabash joined the Tippecanoe. Tippecanoe, a derivation of a Potawatomi word Kehtipaquononk, means a "great clearing".

The Indians were farther from the whites here, the land had never been subject to a treaty between Indians and Americans, and the rich Wabash River bottoms could have produced enough corn to feed all the tribes of the old Northwest. The settlement became known as "The Prophet's Town", and scores of new houses went up.

The situation was a hard one for Harrison. He had fumed constantly when the Prophet and his followers were on "the sacred soil of Greenville". Now they were just up the river from him, on land that had no treaty rights for the Americans.

Both British and American officials followed the Tippecanoe venture with interest. The British agent at Fort Malden on the Detroit River reported to his superior in the Indian department the Prophet's move, adding that "he expects a visit from thirty different nations from the southward and westward of the Mississippi". Harrison's agent, pretending to look for stolen horses, reported every move to his employer.

There was peace, comfort, and prospect of plenty at the Prophet's Town. Tecumseh could leave it and devote himself entirely to the majestic design that had occupied his mind and heart for years now.

His grand concept was the union of all the Indian tribes in North America in one vast confederacy, one invincible union. All the red men must see that their salvation, their only hope to save their country (what was left of it), their self-respect, and their own civilization lay in their joining together. Together they could hold the white horde at bay. All Indian tribes must be alerted, all must be persuaded. Tecumseh, orator, warrior, statesman, and visionary, would be the voice of their salvation. He set out in the autumn of 1808 to make his magnificent dream come true.

He went from Lake Superior to the Gulf of Mexico, from his own Scioto country to the waters of the Arkansas and the Missouri. He spent almost all of the next four years ranging the Indian land, on foot, by canoe, on horseback. No Indian, before or since, has made such a far-reaching and at the same time such an important journey. Pontiac, seeking allies, had sent messengers to the tribes. Tecumseh visited them himself.

The Prophet and Billy Caldwell, the Jesuit-trained half-breed whom the Indians called Straight Tree, and a few others were with the chief in the beginning. Mounted on fast ponies, they began the mighty pilgrimage. As they moved across the plain, they hunted and fished. Nuts, grapes, berries, and wild plums were abundant. Sometimes when the cold became too severe, they lived as guests among friendly tribes. Sometimes they took a wide swing that brought them back to Tippecanoe for the fiercest part of the winter.

As they moved from tribe to tribe their band increased. The Potawatomi responded to Tecumseh's words, and one of the noblest chiefs, the tall Shabbona, joined the travellers. He became an enduring strength to Tecumseh, a man of his own kind. Black Hawk, of the Sauk, promised that the Sauk would enter Tecumseh's confederacy. In the Iroquois country the Prophet was silent. The Iroquois had an active prophet of their own, Handsome Lake. Prophets are known not to agree, or even to tolerate each other, in the same territory. From the time of this first journey to the tribes, the Prophet retired more and more into the background. Tenskwautawau's voice was silent when Tecumseh spoke.

The Kickapoo, made famous by their talent for lightning raids and their harvest of stolen horses, listened with strong approval to Tecumseh, and swore to hold all their land against the Americans.

The great Shawnee met with some reverses. The Miami could not be quite shaken from their allegiance to Little Turtle. They no longer respected him fully because of his soft life on an American annuity, but would not swear to join the tribes against the Americans. Some faint-hearted tribes too fond of whisky would not listen to the message of hope because it might mean war. The Onondaga and Seneca of the Iroquois would follow no chief but their own.

On the whole, Tecumseh was amazingly successful. Pontiac's old tribe, the Ottawa, listened to the visionary program of Tecumseh and accepted him as their leader. Two hundred Ottawa chiefs and warriors left their villages and took their squaws and children to Tippecanoe. Shawnee, Potawatomi, Chippewa, Fox, Sauk, Delaware, Winnibago, Kickapoo, and – most spectacular success of all – the elder brother of the tribes, the fighting Wyandot, promised to stand with Tecumseh with all or part of their strength.

Some of the battling Sioux and a few groups from the Seneca, the Miami, and the Illinois who did not follow him wholeheartedly promised help when the war belt should be passed.

Red Jacket of the Seneca, old now and feeble, but one of the greatest warriors of all time, fingered the great medal George Washington had given him, and shook his head.

Tecumseh was fairly content with his mission, and now the call of home was strong within him. They all needed the peace and security of the Wabash. The tired horses, looking for rest, jogged hopefully on, needing no persuasion, smelling the fields of home.

A day from home, Tecumseh suddenly drew his horse to

a halt. Over the horizon, a single, tiny moving object was coming towards them. A horseman, they saw, and one of their own. The rider was one of a band of Shawnee warriors who had fanned out over the immensity of the plains to find their leader. He brought terrifying news. Harrison, using the mellowing influence of keg after keg of whisky, had, in the phrase he was so fond of using, "extinguished Indian titles" – to the extent of three million acres on the White River and in the rich valley of the Wabash.

No Shawnee had been to the treaty-making. No Shawnee name had been signed. But the land! The land was gone!

Harrison, acting as President Jefferson's agent, operated on one single order, "Get the land". Jefferson wrote, "What is the right of a huntsman to the thousand miles over which he has accidentally ranged in search of prey? Is one of the fairest portions of the globe to remain in a state of nature, the haunt of a few wretched savages, when it seems destined by the Creator to give support to a large population, and to be the seat of civilization, of science and true religion?"

And yet, the land between Vincennes and the Ohio was not by any means filled in. Many white people did not see the need for this vast new extension that Harrison had procured.

President Jefferson presented various schemes, whose sole end was "Get the land". The Indians were to be persuaded to cultivate the land instead of hunting over it. "Nothing is so easy to learn as to cultivate the earth – all your women understand it." He doubly insulted the Indian – was he to trade his tomahawk for a hoe, learn to be a squaw? Jefferson invited the Indian to exchange freedom for slavery, the wild wonderful hunt for the necessity of pecking away in a small patch of earth. Such a change would be death to Tecumseh's men, to every Indian who ranged the plains and raced the rivers.

The oncoming settlers themselves were far from approving Jefferson's idea of making farmers out of warriors. They feared that if the Indians had enough to eat from farming, they would have more time to give to raiding settlements for entertainment.

"Get the land," said Jefferson. Nothing must interfere. After learning to be farmers, "they will perceive how useless to them are extensive forests . . . we shall push our trading houses and be glad to see the good and influential among them in debt, because we observe that when these debts get beyond what the individuals can pay, they become willing to lop them off by a cession of lands."

But the Indians could not understand that Jefferson loved them, and wished only to do them good by taking their land from them!

Harrison understood the president very well, and served him well. The Treaty of Fort Wayne, 1809, brought three million acres of land, worth six million dollars, to his government. The Indians, "mellow with wine", the little chiefs, most of them of tribes not even hunting over the land that their drunken assent passed to the Americans, could not read the terms of the treaty. A map was drawn of their latest grant to the white men. The line to the north-west and the line to the north made an angle as of the hands of a clock pointing to the hour of ten. It became known as the Ten O'Clock Treaty.

Tecumseh rode fiercely home to find that the work was done. Once again, as it had been done hundreds of times before, promise or no promise, treaty or no treaty, Indian land had been bartered away by people who had no right to barter it, whose chiefs had vowed to barter no more.

Tecumseh was enraged for the insult to his Shawnee. For generations they had hunted over this land. They had been given no chance to refuse the treaty. The wretched little chiefs, the worn-out, feeble, little chiefs, who reached for a whisky keg and signed this thing, would die for it. The land must be restored to the Indians. The annuities must not be accepted. The Ten O'Clock Treaty, the Treaty of Fort Wayne, signed in the autumn of 1809, brought Tecumseh long thoughts of the British redcoats. It started furious activity in the Prophet's Town.

Hundreds of Indians descended upon the Tippecanoe. The Prophet's following grew to a thousand warriors by the spring. The Tippecanoe Indians were preparing to prevent any more encroachment on their territory. There were fierce games and dancing; the chips flew from the stone, and the piles of arrowheads grew.

Harrison, up in his beautiful home "Grouselands", constantly studying Roman military history, grew very uneasy about the state of affairs in the Prophet's Town. His spies, pretending to be traders, brought disturbing news. Winamac, a Potawatomi chief who had helped Harrison persuade the little chiefs to sign the Ten O'Clock Treaty, told his master that Tecumseh meant to have the land back, that the great Wyandot were Tecumseh's men now, and that at this very moment, no doubt, a great massacre was being planned. Winamac did not discourage Harrison in his belief that there were British guns and ammunition added to the arrowheads.

Harrison wrote a letter to the Prophet, whom he still thought of as the brains of the Tippecanoe town. He said if he, the Prophet, could prove ownership of the Ten O'Clock lands, they would be restored, and the treaty rescinded. It was an insulting and empty gesture. Possession could be proved only by occupancy. How could the Indians survey and "occupy" their hunting-grounds?

The interpreter, Joseph Barron, was taken to the Prophet's reception room, where the miracle worker sat on a raised throne and received the interpreter coldly. Tecumseh stood, arms folded, his face stern and impassive, listening. Warriors and squaws formed an interested audience. The Prophet's wife, a woman of violent passions, fastened her black gaze on the interpreter's face. Barron's escort armed and uneasy, was kept immobile at the back of the room. The Prophet spoke in cold anger. "For what purpose do you come here? Brouillette was here . . . he was a spy. Dubois was here . . . he was a spy. Now *you* have come. You too are a spy. There is your grave." He pointed to the ground at Barron's feet. "Look on it!"

The interpreter paled and the warriors stirred. But Tecum-

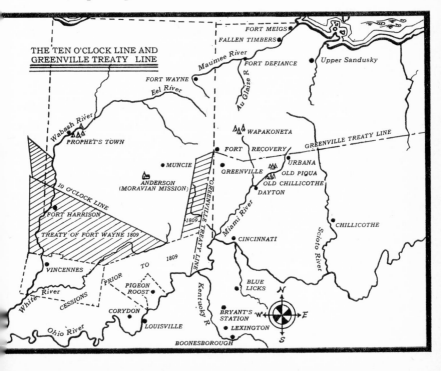

seh lifted his hand, "You are in no danger," he said, handing Barron the letter. "Read."

The letter invited the Prophet and three chiefs to make a visit to President Jefferson in Washington. There, Harrison thought, the hot, warlike spirit might die at the sight of the bluecoats "more numerous than you can count, and our hunting shirts like the leaves of the forest, or the grains of sand on the Wabash".

Tecumseh interrupted. "I myself will go to Vincennes."

The meeting was over. Tecumseh took Barron to his own tent.

The two men talked for hours. Tecumseh told Barron that he would come to see Harrison about the Ten O'Clock Treaty, which was no treaty, and that unless the American settlers ceased to encroach, he could no longer be a friend to them.

When he had finished, Tecumseh said, "It is not safe for you to stay here. The women plan to kill you as you sleep. Come with me." The chief led Barron away from the village to a steep ravine. He gave the call of a wild turkey. At this, Barron's horse and two others were led out of the woods. The spy and interpreter, the envoy of the enemy, went back to his master in "safe conduct".

Three hundred warriors set out down the Wabash to Harrison at Vincennes. Eighty canoes, well furnished with war clubs and tomahawks, carried the braves. They were stripped, but for deerskin breeches, and painted with bright vermilion war paint. Only the scalp-lock remained of their hair. Tecumseh, in his simple deerskin costume, an eagle feather thrust into the handkerchief he wore over his head, led the party. His brother the Prophet travelled with him, wearing the ceremonial black robe and raven wings symbolic of his religious status.

The town of Vincennes was prepared for the visitors. A troop of dragoons under arms, a cavalry detachment, and two companies of foot soldiers as reinforcements in case of trouble with Tecumseh's warriors, were stationed just outside the village. Bayonets glinted along Main Street in the August sun.

Harrison had prepared a meeting-place in a canopied arbour at the side of his house. The chairs were set out for him and his party – guards, ladies, judges of the Supreme Court of Indiana, and other dignitaries. A well-armed platoon under the command of a sergeant formed his honour guard.

Tecumseh, with thirty of his spectacular warriors, advanced towards the meeting-place. He looked at the men before him, all armed with pistols, singly or in pairs. "Side arms" had been the agreement between Tecumseh and Harrison. Harrison, although a vain, ambitious, and scheming man with an insatiable hunger for Indian land, was no coward. His only weapon was a sword.

About thirty paces from the Governor's party, Tecumseh suddenly stopped. His warriors, wary as cats, hands on tomahawks, stopped at the same instant, looking at their leader for a sign. Were they to rush in and scalp these white men? Tecumseh looked with extreme disfavour on the arrangement of awning and porch. He said to Barron, again his interpreter, "Houses are made for white men to hold their councils in, Indians hold theirs in the open air."

Harrison beckoned to Tecumseh to sit beside him. "Your father," said Barron, "wishes you to sit beside him."

"My father!" Tecumseh exclaimed in ringing scornful tones. "The Great Spirit is my father. The earth is my mother and on her bosom I will recline." He seated himself, and his warriors sat cross-legged behind him. Tecumseh pointed to a grove of trees a little distance from the house. It seemed that the great Indian would be content to hold council there. Barron protested at the trouble it would be to move the chairs there. The Shawnee remarked easily that only white people needed chairs, Indians sat on the ground.

Far from pleased, the whole party, chairs and all, removed to the shade of the trees. Harrison spoke first. He wanted, he said, to talk to Tecumseh about the settler-Indian situation. He wondered if it might be possible for a spokesman from the tribes to visit the President. Then the skies opened and a torrential rain sent the conference running for shelter.

Rain and Tecumseh's whims, the necessity he felt for making his oration as striking, persuasive, and shapely as possible, kept Vincennes in a state of nervous apprehension for nine days. Then the mighty Shawnee spoke.

He reviewed the history of the relations of the whites

and Indians. He accused the Americans at this moment of fomenting discord among the Indians, of trying to force them into being responsible for trouble. "You endeavour to prevent the Indians from forming their confederacy, although your Seventeen Fires have joined in one union.

"As soon as this council is over, I shall go on a visit to the tribes in the south, which I have not yet had time to do, because of the troubles on the Tippecanoe and the signing of the evil treaty. It is a false treaty, without meaning. It was signed by a few, poor, weak, foolish, worn-out chiefs who have no rights any more among the Indians. All is now in the hands of the warriors," he added menacingly.

Tecumseh looked coldly at Harrison. "In one moon, or two, we shall have a great meeting. All these chiefs will be brought together. If by that time the land which the false treaty gave away has not been returned to its true owners,

the Indians, we shall kill those chiefs. It will be your hand which is red with their blood."

Harrison swallowed hard and looked at Winamac, the Potawatomi. Tecumseh pointed a long, accusing finger at the traitor to his people. "There sits the black dog that makes lies and tells them, to cause white men and red men to hate each other!" Winamac laid his hand on his gun.

But Tecumseh had no ammunition to spare for such a contemptible being. His business was with Harrison. He put questions to the Governor that he was embarrassed at having to answer. He had thought of Tecumseh as a supplicant. The Shawnee chief quite obviously considered himself as of the same rank and condition as the Governor, if not of a higher. Harrison was the servant of the President. Tecumseh was no man's servant. He was the voice of the Indian calling on the white man to explain his action. His thirty warriors squatted behind him, still as stone, while he spoke, standing.

"Once my people were a happy race. Now they are made miserable by the white people who are always encroaching. The land never was divided, but belongs to all, for the use of everyone. No groups among us have a right to sell even to one another, much less to strangers who want all."

Harrison shifted uncomfortably. This was not the kind of thing he had hoped to show to his guests. "Brother," Tecumseh went on, "I was glad to hear your speech. You said if we could show that the land was sold by persons who had no right to sell, you would restore it. . . ." The chief's great voice filled the grove. "Oh, that I might make the fortunes of my red people and of my country as great as the conceptions of my mind, when I think of the Great Spirit who rules this universe! I would not then come to Governor Harrison and ask him to tear up the treaty and obliterate the landmarks. I would say to him, 'Sire, you have permission to return to your own country.' Sell a country! Why not sell the air, the clouds, and the great sea? Did not the Great Spirit make them all for the use of His children?"

After an effective pause Tecumseh asked Harrison what he meant to do about the land. His answer was feeble. He said that the Shawnee had come from Georgia in the south and could have no claim on the Wabash country, which was really Miami land.

"It is not Miami, nor Shawnee, nor Potawatomi," said Tecumseh sternly. "It is Indian land."

Then the chief was silent, and listened while Harrison claimed fair usage with the Indians on the part of the Americans. Tecumseh needed no interpreter to understand English – Rebecca Galloway had prepared him well. But because the Shawnee would never speak in English to an American, an interpreter was translating as Harrison spoke. Harrison gave chapter and verse for the amount of money the Indians had received from the generous hands of the Americans. Before the translation came through, Tecumseh was on his feet in a flaming passion. "He lies! He lies!"

He poured violent and picturesque Shawnee abuse on the Governor. His warriors leapt to their feet and flashed their tomahawks. Twelve riflemen rushed to cover Harrison. The Governor, not understanding the words, but realizing that there had been insult, drew his sword. For one electric moment it seemed that there might be massacre. But the chief recovered himself and the warriors dropped their hands. Harrison declared the council over and led his terrified guests back into the safety of his house.

Dead Chief of the Potawatomi, who was deaf, saw Tecumseh lash out at Harrison. He saw the angry faces and the hands jump to guns and swords. When the mad moment had passed and politeness and protocol triumphed, friends made known to Dead Chief what Tecumseh had said to the Governor. Dead Chief was angry, and trotted about Vincennes boasting of what he would have done had he known what the Shawnee had called the Governor. The warriors among the Potawatomi advised him to be still. But Dead Chief, seeing the streets full of soldiers, all surely enemies of Tecumseh, would not be still.

In the evening, while Barron was in Tecumseh's tent setting down the text of his oration correctly, Dead Chief came whooping defiance. He was armed with war club, rifle, and scalping-knife. He had put on his feather head-dress and his black and vermilion war paint. He rushed from the river up to Tecumseh's tent. Tecumseh did not give him a glance.

It was important for the record that his speech should be correctly written down. Sometimes he spoke with such heat and with such flights of imagery that even the best of interpreters failed. The Shawnee went on talking to Barron in a low tone. The furious Dead Chief brandished his tomahawk, and yelled insult and threat to Tecumseh.

"You and your men," he said, "can kill the white man's hogs and call them bears but you dare not face a warrior. *Squaw!*"

The mighty Shawnee scorned to pay any attention to the frenzied man, and merely made one slight motion of his head to a warrior. Boasting and vainglorious Dead Chief ran back to his canoe. He paddled to Vincennes, shouting his triumph to the white men at the dock, and then into the darkness beyond. He was never seen again.

Almost a year after his first visit Tecumseh came again down the Wabash. The land question had not been settled, the purchases were not completed. The treaty-signing chiefs still lived in fear. Terror of Indian attack flamed through the settlements, and rumours flew of the war to be between Indian and white when the corn was ripe.

In the summer of 1811, two Potawatomi murdered four white men. Harrison demanded that Tecumseh come and account for the murder. With nearly two hundred warriors, armed with knives and tomahawks, bows and arrows, Tecumseh came.

The council began in the afternoon and ended with the moon high in the sky. Tecumseh refused to hand over his Potawatomi. Indians were frequently murdered and no white man suffered for the murder. And what about any restoration of the lands? The return of the lands was in the hands of the President, Harrison told the Shawnee. "As the great chief over the mountains is to decide the matter," Tecumseh said, "I hope the Great Spirit will put sense enough in his head to order you to give up those lands. It is true, he may sit in his fine house and drink his wine while you and I have to fight it out."

Harrison lost his temper with this insolent man. The President, he said, would put his warriors in petticoats sooner than give up a country he had fairly acquired from its rightful owners.

The American Secretary of War had long thought that the best thing to be done with both Tecumseh and the Prophet was to seize them and put them in prison. It must have been a tempting thought to Harrison as he saw the arrogant figure of the great chief before him. But behind Tecumseh, those fierce fully-armed warriors waited, and back in their clearings in the forest were the trembling settlers. Harrison knew that their lives would be short and bloody if the Long Knives dared to take the chief. He broke off the meeting.

Tecumseh, the Prophet, the warriors, wives, children,

tomahawks, and bows and arrows moved out again on the bosom of the Wabash, and Vincennes breathed once more. Harrison watched them go, a hungry, primitive, childish people, with a near genius as their leader. He pondered on the chief's last words: "I go now to the south." Then he went slowly back to his beautiful library in Grouselands, and wrote one of the great long letters that he showered on his superiors, on the War Department, and even on the governors of the neighbouring states.

". . . there can be no doubt that his object is to excite the southern Indians to war. His mother was of the Creek nation, and he builds much upon that circumstance. . . . I do not think there is any danger of further hostility until he returns; his absence affords a most favourable opportunity for breaking up his confederacy. . . . The implicit obedience and respect which the followers of Tecumseh pay him is really astonishing, and more than any other circumstance bespeaks him as one of those uncommon geniuses which spring up occasionally to produce revolutions and overturn the established order of things. No difficulties deter him. For four years he had been in constant motion. You see him to-day on the Wabash, and in a short time hear of him on the shores of Lake Erie . . . or on the banks of the Mississippi; and wherever he goes he makes an impression favourable to his purposes. He is now upon the last round to put a finishing strike to his work. I hope, however, before his return that that part of the fabric which he considered complete will be demolished, and even its foundations rooted up." He thought that the Romans would have approved of his strategy.

Like a tune that would not go out of his head the chief's last words haunted Harrison: "I go now to the south."

6. Journey to the Midday

Tecumseh visited the tribes in Ohio, Indiana, and Michigan, strengthening old bonds, forging new ones. Before he set out to the south he journeyed to the British at Fort Malden. He spoke formally to a large gathering on the parade-ground there. When he had left, the British sifted direct statement from imagery and concluded that the Indian was certainly preparing for war. He showed a wampum belt that was symbolic, he said, of the joint destiny of the red and the white people. "We are now men," he said, "and think ourselves capable of defending our country. . . . We expect that you will forward to us what will be necessary to supply our wants. . . . I intend to go towards the midday sun and expect before next autumn that the business will be done."

Apprehensive British officers, who wanted no part of a war pact against the Americans at that moment, questioned the chief as to the meaning of his words. He meant only, Tecumseh said, that his confederacy would then be complete.

Jim Blue Jacket, son of the great chief Blue Jacket, was Tecumseh's chief lieutenant as he paddled towards his mother's people to enlist them in his confederacy. The Prophet and the giant faithful Potawatomi, Shabbona, were left on guard at Tippecanoe.

For six months the troupe travelled, covering thousands of miles by swift pony, on foot, and by canoe. The braves wore the simple buckskin suits that Tecumseh ordered as suitable for Indian warriors who depended upon Indian weapons and Indian ways. Tecumseh held that in theory all would be well with the red men if they shed all white advantage and lived, hunted, and dressed as their forefathers had done. But each of his warriors, besides his tomahawk and scalping-knife, carried a rifle too. And there was some glory in their ornaments. Their heads were shaved, but all wore a three-inch band of scarlet flannel with touches of silver bound about their foreheads. Their scalp-locks were braided

in three plaits that hung between their shoulders, and hawk feathers were thrust into the band about their heads. Silver gorgets hung from their necks and silver bands clasped their wrists and arms. Painted red circles showed on their temples and breasts, and stripes of red paint were drawn below their eyes and across the high cheek-bones.

Tecumseh wore two symbolic crane feathers, one white to show that he came in peace, and one red that he was ready for war. His silver gorget lay on his chest, a mighty ornament on a mighty chest.

The warrior band visited the Choctaw, the Muskogee, the Creek, the Seminole, and the Osage. Echoes of Tecumseh's oratory still ring across the Mississippi and the Tallapoosa. In words of flame he denounced the white man who was stealing the land from the red. He adjured the Indians to unite against the whites, to keep from tribal war, to drink no white man's whisky, and to practise kindness always to women and children. He told them that the Americans and the British would soon be at war, and that they must join the British.

The tribes listened to him. The young men jumped to their feet, tomahawks flashing. But the chiefs would not join him against the Americans. The Chickasaw, a mere remnant of a mighty tribe, were rich and comfortable on their lands. Some of them even had slaves of their own, and had long ago ceased to be hunters or fighters. The great Choctaw, their neighbours, were pleased to listen to Tecumseh, but they had been established for many years on their land, had permanent towns, and had no intention of leaving them. Their greatest chief, Pushmataha, a warrior with fantastic legends growing about him, became Tecumseh's shadow and adversary.

Where Tecumseh travelled in the Choctaw country, there travelled Pushmataha too. He would not permit the Shawnee dance to open a council. The Choctaw dance introduced Tecumseh's meeting.

Tecumseh urged the Choctaw to enter the Indian confederacy, to join the British and make war on the Americans. Pushmataha turned on him, commanded silence, and spoke to his people. "The winds howled, the rain fell, the thunder roared, and the lightning flashed; a pine tree was shivered and from its splinters Pushmataha stepped forth with a rifle in his hand. When our fathers took the hand of Washington they told him the Choctaw would always be the friends of his people. Listen to the voice of prudence ere you rashly act! I shall join your friends the Americans in this war."

The Creek and the Chickasaw, the Choctaw, and the Osage, to whom he went over the Great Smokies, refused to lift their tomahawks. The Muskogee and the Seminole agreed that he had a good idea, but would not commit themselves. The hazardous heart-breaking journey was done. There was little accomplished. The southern tribes were too soft, rich, and comfortable. They would not be stirred.

Tecumseh turned homeward. For six months he had been without news of Tippecanoe. He knew now that the northern tribes must unite even more firmly than ever if they were to turn the white man back. The British might even now be on the war-path. Shabbona might have gathered in more recruits while he had been away. More tribes might be waiting to greet him. The thought of Tippecanoe and his faithful followers there, the virtues of the place itself as the heart of the confederacy, as a launching-ground for the war for justice to the red man, heartened him as he came near his home.

Tecumseh and his warriors paddled swiftly up the Wabash to the Prophet's Town. Soon, after another bend, and another mile, the roofs of home would show. By now the corn would be gathered in the storehouses, the wood piled in great heaps against the winter. Tecumseh and his men lifted their eyes to see the first smoke from a cooking-fire.

There was no smoke. There were no storehouses. There were no dwellings. The Prophet's Town was not there at all. Only acres of charred earth lay where the town had stood.

7. Disaster at Tippecanoe

THE IDEA of the dangers of Tippecanoe, of its Prophet, of its potentiality for trouble grew in Harrison's brain like a poisonous mushroom. He showered letters on Mr. Madison, the new President, stressing the menace of the concentration of Indians on the Wabash. In answer to each battle-kindling letter, the President sent a peaceful response. On no account was there to be trouble between the Americans and the Indians. Madison commented on the existing uneasy relations between the British and the Americans. Unless, he said, the Prophet's people openly attacked the Americans there was to be peace, unbroken peace, between the white man and the red.

Harrison sent daily letters for a while to the War Department, assuring them that the time was at hand when the tribes would fall on the white men. Steps must be taken, preparations made to prevent any possible Indian successes.

All was peaceful on the Tippecanoe. But Harrison had persuaded himself that it was his patriotic duty for the good of the United States to destroy the settlement. The deed must be done, the Indians scattered. And it must be done soon, while Tecumseh was away.

The best time to "root up the Prophet's Town" would be just after the harvest. The stored corn would be easily destroyed, the land laid waste, and the Indians left with neither shelter nor prospect of food for the winter. Since the President would not realize the menace, it was up to the Governor, the man on the job, to see to the necessary, if distasteful, business.

In October, Harrison crossed the Wabash and Vermilion rivers and invaded Indian territory. With nearly a thousand men he moved through the land that no treaty had ever conveyed to the Americans. The Governor was an invader. He was the aggressor, a treaty-breaker, establishing himself and his armed men where they had no right to be. Had the provisions of the treaty of Greenville really worked fairly for the Indian signers of it, then the United States forces should have been at Tippecanoe fighting off Harrison and protecting the Prophet. But there was never much justice for the red man.

Harrison, the invader, asked advice of the Indians for the placing of his camp. Wood, water, shelter, and good defence were his requirements. Almost more strangely, the Indians gave him excellent advice. Yet each side knew that they were foes, and that very shortly, unless Tecumseh came, there would be bloodletting.

Provoked too often by the Long Knives' operations almost in their own camp, the braves went out of the Prophet's control. Nor could Shabbona persuade them to always be peaceable and quiet. They plotted against Harrison, and at last he had his wish. The Indians attacked. A party of Indian braves crawled through the long grass with the intention of silencing the American sentries for ever. The plan was to press then into Harrison's quarters and deal death to him. But just as dawn broke, a stir in the lush grass caught a sentry's eye. He raised his rifle and shot. An Indian screamed in his sudden agony and the whole American camp was alerted. Harrison, an early riser, put on his other boot and the most important of all his battles began.

From the beginning, of course, there was no hope for the Indians. They had no recognized leader and no talent for fighting as a unit. The Prophet, true to his principle of fighting no wars, had kept a shipment of rifles still unpacked. Bearing the battle arms of their fathers the Indians fell on the enemy. The Prophet stood on a little hill and chanted. Each Indian for himself and mad with excitement, ill-advised, hasty, and helpless in the face of American steel and American discipline, they were defeated in little more than two hours. But sixty-one Americans lay dead, half as many Indians. The scalps of the dead Indians were harvested by the enemy.

Harrison lived. He customarily rode a grey horse, and the red men knew him by it. In the first flush of battle, he jumped on a bay horse, the nearest to his hand. One of his officers mounted the grey and was dead in minutes.

Tippecanoe was not a great battle. It was neither decisive nor necessary. Only the physical centre of Tecumseh's confederacy was destroyed; his resolution to take his warriors over to the service of the British was strengthened.

But the years of peace, of security from Indian menace were over. Settlers in Indiana, who had lived safely for years, rushed to the blockhouses for asylum from the roving bands of furious Indians. Scalpings and murders became common again. Within five miles of Vincennes, a whole family was wiped out. A score of new forts had to be built to keep the white men safe.

For Harrison the Battle of Tippecanoe was one of the greatest military and strategic battles ever fought in the western world. Its importance, and his importance with it, grew with every passing day, "His vanity more than fermented, it blubbered over," said a Kentucky lawyer who knew him.

In the years to come, Tippecanoe made Harrison President of the United States. "Old Tippecanoe", they called him. He wore the infamous nickname as if it were a garland of roses.

8. War Between the White Men

TECUMSEH threw the Prophet out of his camp. The days of his grandeur were over; he was not worthy of trust. Perhaps he had not ordered the braves into their unequal battle, but he had not kept them from it. In his weakness he had allowed the Indian position to be immeasurably weakened. He had put the red men in the position of starting a war. The Indian shots came first.

The Shawnee chief knew when his journeying to the south was done that there would never be enough tribes solidly joined in common purpose to fight the aggressive Americans without the aid of the British. Their only hope would be to join with the British if ever their dream of a land of their own could be realized.

In the ashes of the ruined Prophet's Town, Tecumseh built a hut, and called the tribes to him. Smoke signals rose from hilltop to hilltop: "Tecumseh has come home." The braves from twelve tribes came to him.

The air was filled with rumours of war. All talk turned to Tippecanoe. Tecumseh's men sharpened their arrowheads. They had little left to fight with and there was to be fighting. They would meet Kentucky rifles with Indian bows and arrows if help did not come to them.

In the spring of 1812, all over Indiana and Ohio and

Michigan, Indian tribes met in council. On the Mississinewa River where it meets the Wabash, a dozen tribes of the North-west Indians met. Here came the chiefs of the Wyandot, the Chippewa, the terrible Potawatomi who had fomented Tippecanoe, Miami, Delaware, and Shawnee.

The Crane, fierce old chief of the Wyandot, threw the blame for the Tippecanoe battle on the Indians. The Wyandot, "elder brothers" of the tribes, commanded respect. But Tecumseh flung the blame squarely on Harrison, at the same time accusing the "pretended" chiefs of the Potawatomi of behaving badly. He had enjoined them to keep peace until such time as he should give the signal. When the time was ripe Tecumseh would "stamp his foot", and the red men should swarm on the war-path, but they must not be alone.

Two days after the conclave on the Wabash, Tecumseh with warriors from the Ottawa, Potawatomi, Winnebago, Sauk and Fox tribes started for Fort Malden, the British fort at Amherstburg. The Indian agent there, Colonel Matthew Elliott, received the Shawnee and his delegation with courtesy. Tecumseh made a stirring speech which the British officers understood to mean that the Indians were ready to go to war with the Americans.

Consternation spread through the British colony. Elliott was troubled enough as it was, to provide for the thousands of friendly Indians who crowded around British forts for food and ammunition. The fur trade was in a very depressed condition and unless the British gave them ammunition they could not hunt food for themselves, and the business would go from bad to worse. An Indian war would dry up the stream of furs, perhaps entirely. It was the British policy to keep the Indians equipped to hunt, to feed them if possible when they were hungry, and to keep them at peace and bringing in the furs.

The British urged peace on Tecumseh and his men.

But now an army of Americans was crawling through the swampy land and woods of northern Ohio. Twelve hundred Ohio militia were on their way to Detroit, Tecumseh's scouts reported. Tecumseh asked the British to support his idea of falling on the marchers. The formal British rejected the offer. The decision seemed a senseless one to the Indians.

Brigadier-General William Hull led the Americans. He was an old man, incompetent, jittery, and terrified of Indians. He had served long in the Revolutionary War, but now "the tooth of time, whisky, and tobacco" had unnerved him.

On the 18th of June, 1812, war was formally declared between the British and the Americans. The war-hawks had pushed the reluctant Madison into war.

Indians suddenly became people of great importance. The Americans hoped at first to keep them neutral. The British enthusiastically prepared to take them as allies. Competition for Indian loyalty and support began the instant war was declared.

There was to be a great council at Fort Wayne. Agents of the American government had news of the utmost importance to Indians. Envoys from General Hull came to Tecumseh. He was especially invited to be there. He was to be told to keep his hands off the white man's war. Hull was vehement in his opinion. This war had nothing to do with Indians. There was to be no hideous Indian warfare, no scalping, no treachery.

Tecumseh travelled to Fort Wayne with two hundred warriors. The Wyandot chief Isadore in council favoured neutrality, under protection of the Long Knives, for the pro-British tribes. Tecumseh answered him contemptuously, "And who will protect you when the Long Knives are fighting the British? Who, when your ancient enemies, the western tribes, are allied with the British?" He dashed the pipe of peace into pieces, and flung them on the ground.

At the second council Tecumseh said, "Here is a chance

which will never come again. It is a chance for all the Indians to join the British. Should they conquer and once
more get the mastery of all this land, our rights to at least a
portion of the land of our fathers would be respected by the
king. . . . If all the land should pass into the hands of the
Americans our last hunting-ground will be taken from us."

The Wyandot were silent. "You are cowards!" Tecumseh
took the pipe again from Isadore and broke it in his hands.
He flung the pieces at the foot of the Wyandot chief.

"Crack! Whoo!" yelled the warriors.

"Do you mean, then," said Isadore, "that you are going to
war against the Americans?"

"I will not stand on neutral ground with you," said Tecumseh, "when the Redcoats and the Long Knives fight."

But he could not allow dissension between the Wyandot
and the Shawnee. They must be united; all tribes must be of
one mind. At midnight the chiefs conferred in Isadore's
tent, a peace-pipe was smoked by both the chiefs, and a
ceremonial hatchet buried. And when the hatchet was
buried, Isadore went back to tell the tale to General Hull.
Tecumseh, followed by large numbers of Shawnee, Kickapoo, Potawatomi, and Delaware, set out for Fort Malden to
meet Colonel Elliott there. He took his people to the island
of Bois Blanc in the Detroit River, close to Malden.

Just across the river in the Wyandot village of Brownstown, General Hull was calling another council. The Crane
assembled here the chiefs who were friendly to the Americans. Here they swore to be neutral. But some of the Wyandot were wavering. Roundhead, Morrow, and Splitlog joined
the British. Walk-in-the-Water swore neutrality, but had to
go to tell Colonel Elliott about it. He reminded Elliott of
that terrible time when the treacherous British had closed
the gates at Miami. Elliott threatened him with prison if he

heard any more such "American talk". But he permitted him to go back to the American side.

Tecumseh's answer to an urgent invitation to General Hull's council was brief and firm.

"No. I have taken my side with the King, my father, and I will suffer my bones to bleach on this shore before I will recross that stream to join in any council of neutrality."

On that night, Tecumseh, with Roundhead, a British officer, and Tecumseh's old friend and aide Billy Caldwell, led a Wyandot detachment across the river. They surrounded Brownstown and brought all its inhabitants as prisoners to Fort Malden.

The die was now cast, the drums of war rolled, and Tecumseh faced his destiny. The passionate orator became the inspired war chief. The old, soft, indolent chiefs who fawned on the Americans and could not see the vision he held before them must fawn still and be blind. The tribes who sat in comfort or on the edge of want, existing upon American charity, must stay as charitable objects. Those who wavered like a breeze between fighting and not fighting, between fear of enemy tribes and faith in their protectors would hear his voice no more.

Every sense was now alerted in the Shawnee chief. All the training that his forty-four years had given him was now to be called upon. He must plan, he must design, he must attack and repulse. He was the acclaimed chief of the Indians at war with the Americans, an ally of the British.

The tribes gathered, ready to fight under the Shawnee chief. Black Hawk of the Sauk brought Sauk and Fox from the upper Mississippi. The Wyandot who were not sworn to neutrality came to Tecumseh from Ohio and were joined by Canadian Wyandot. Chippewa, Kickapoo, and the violent Potawatomi swelled the forces on the Canadian side. It is thought that from time to time during the war there were from a thousand to three thousand red men on the Canadian bank of the river. And with them, in the Indian way, there came their families, women and children, babies, old men, all of whom had to be fed.

The British garrison was a very small one, and providing as much as twelve thousand rations a day was an enormous problem. Many of the Indians were in the course of time to die from malnutrition, and many were to freeze to death.

During late June and early July Tecumseh's scouts slipped as noiselessly as shadows through the woods, waiting and watching to see what Hull and his army would do. The nervous old man and his army reached Detroit unmolested. On the twelfth of July he invaded Canada with three thousand men. Cavalry and artillery trotted and clanked through the streets of Sandwich, and General Hull broadcast his heroic proclamation:

"Inhabitants of Canada! After thirty years of peace and prosperity the United States have been driven to Arms. The injuries and aggressions, the insults and indignities of Great Britain have once more left them no alternative but manly resistance . . . if the barbarous and savage policy of Great Britain be pursued, and the savages are let loose to murder our Citizens and butcher our women and children, this war will be a war of extermination. The first stroke with the tomahawk, the first attempt with the Scalping Knife will be the signal for one indiscriminate scene of desolations. No white man found fighting by the side of an Indian will be taken prisoner. Instant destruction will be his lot. . . . The United States offer you Peace, Liberty and Security, your choice lies between these and War, Slavery and Destruction. Choose them, but choose wisely. . . ."

It seemed that the way was clear and open for the General. The British garrison at Fort Malden numbered only about three hundred men. Between Hull and Malden there stood only sixteen miles of road, Tecumseh, and his Indians. Hull reasoned, too, that the great majority of the inhabitants of the area were but newly-come Americans. They would flock to his standard and the war would be over, almost before a battle could begin.

Between the two camps, Sandwich and Fort Malden at Amherstburg, there stretched a distance less than a short day's march, a ride on a fast horse for an hour. And once the weak little British fort was demolished, the road to Niagara would be practically cleared for the American. Malden was a tiny fort, totally unable to stand in the face of an attack of artillery. A dry ditch stood about it, and all of its few buildings were frail wooden structures with shingle roofs. One American shell exploding on a shingle roof could have made a burning ruin of Fort Malden. The British commander, Colonel St. George, prepared to evacuate it when the Americans should come; it could not be defended.

But the Americans did not come. Hull dithered and hedged and put off the attack. His officers and men grew ashamed of his attitude. One determined colonel, Lewis Cass, brought a vanguard of Americans to a bridge on the Aux Canards River, within four miles of Fort Malden. He was a clever commander and gained possession of the Aux Canards bridge in spite of the efforts of the British and Tecumseh to fight him off. The ground was marshy, and instead of fighting it out at the bridge, Cass took his men four miles up river, and suddenly came down on the rear of the Indians and the British militia.

The Indians saw the Long Knives coming, and memories of Tippecanoe rose like phantoms about them. They fled in spite of all that Teceumseh could do to restrain them. A few Indians were killed, but no Long Knife was hurt. The Americans were jubilant, and joined Cass at the bridge with a field-piece. They would hold the bridge until Hull could get on towards Fort Malden and capture it. The advance party had ammunition piled in the wagons, and cannon on board a floating battery. They were full of zeal, more than ready to fight. But the presence of all these Indians paralysed Hull. He would not let his main army join Cass. The position was too exposed, he said, and he ordered the victorious few to come back and join the main army again.

The men moved reluctantly off the bridge. The British then tore up its planks and brought in the little warship *Queen Charlotte* to give them protection from the Detroit River side. Tecumseh took a troop of his Indians single file over the remaining bridge beams, harrying the reconnoitring American forces.

General Hull found himself in an awkward situation. His camp was set up among unfriendly people who could not seem to realize that he had come to set them free from British tyranny. He did not dare to send out foraging parties because of those terrible Indians. Hull sent a desperate call to the Governor of Ohio for provisions. He had to send it by land because the British had control of Lake Erie and the freedom of the Detroit River. They could intercept messengers and waylay convoys on the water. A strong guard would be necessary, in any case. The supply route passed in clear view of the British camped on the opposite shore.

Tecumseh crossed over to the American side and dedicated himself to seeing that General Hull got no help from Ohio.

A hundred cattle and wagon-loads of provisions were assembled at Urbana. Captain Henry Brush, with 230 militia and the supplies, marched within thirty-five miles of Detroit. They halted at the River Raisin. Messengers gave Brush the information that Tecumseh and his men were waiting for him at Brownstown. The American sent a fast-riding messenger to Hull asking for troops to protect his precious convoy. Hull thought he would send them, and then he thought he wouldn't. The more he thought about it, the harder it became for him to make up his mind. At last his officers insisted that he send men. He sent a battalion of two hundred under Major Van Horne to rescue Captain Brush's convoy. Van Horne started out early in August. He had with him a great package of dispatches and all the letters that the soldiers in Hull's army had written. They were to be sent on their way when he reached Brush.

Van Horne pressed on towards Brownstown, although he knew that there were hundreds of Indians on the road. Tecumseh and his party stood between Van Horne and Brush. The Shawnee now had Long Knives on both sides of him.

North of Brownstown the road ran between a cornfield and a wooded creek. Silent and invisible, Tecumseh's men waited under cover of cornstalk and thorn bushes. They held their breath as the vanguard, twenty-five picked American soldiers, came to within fifty yards of them. The chief gave his signal and there was a sudden, wholly unexpected volley. Panic swept through the vanguard; the men following them were thrown into confusion. Van Horne, seeing his men running around thrown right out of order by the shooting, tomahawking, whooping Indians who had appeared from nowhere, ordered a retreat. In utter disorder the Americans scrambled back the way they had come. Tecumseh and the Indians pursued the fleeing troops for seven miles up the road to Detroit.

Then Tecumseh, remembering that there was a foe behind him, called off his troops. He turned them back again towards Captain Brush and the convoy on the River Raisin. Seventeen Long Knives, of whom seven were officers, had lost their scalps at Brownstown. At least seventy soldiers were missing. The scalps of the dead fluttered from long poles on the Detroit-Brownstown road. It was a cruel reminder to any American boy who passed that way in search of a part in the Indian wars.

For Tecumseh the cruellest part of the battle was the death of Jim Blue Jacket, his lifelong friend.

Despairing letters from the disgruntled soldiers in Detroit, outspokenly critical of Hull, and dispatches of Hull himself were the most valuable booty. Tecumseh took them across the river at once to the British officers at Fort Malden. They gave a most useful insight into the mind and spirit of the American command, and into the sharply derisive attitude of the soldiers to their woffling general.

The news of the great British victory at Mackinac crushed what little spirit there was left in General Hull. The British and Indians were now in control of Lake Michigan. "... after the surrender of Michilimackinac almost every tribe and nation of Indians . . . joined in open hostility under the British standard, against the Army I commanded. . . . The surrender of Michilimackinac opened the northern hive of Indians and they were swarming down in every direction."

Thus Hull excused his hasty exit from British soil. He

abandoned all his plans for conquering Canada and skulked back to Detroit, carrying with him a thoroughly disgusted army.

He was not very much more comfortable on American soil. Captain Brush's convoy was still down by the River Raisin. Hull ordered a force of six hundred men under Colonel Miller to proceed to the River Raisin and bring the convoy in.

But between the convoy and Detroit there stood Tecumseh. The chief had about two hundred and fifty Indians. Splitlog and Walk-in-the-Water were with him. Walk-in-the-Water, who had earlier been all for neutrality, had grown bored, being left out of the fighting. He was fighting for Tecumseh now, near his home town of Monguaga.

Major Muir with two hundred men, regulars and militia, crossed the river and joined the chief. Tecumseh's runners, spying out the advancing Americans, said they were in numbers "like the mosquitoes of the swamp". Muir asked Colonel Procter, the British commander at Fort Malden, for reinforcements. Sixty men came over.

So Indians and British and Canadians marched to meet the "mosquitoes of the swamp". They planned to attack the American advance at Monguaga, with the white men wearing basswood sprigs in their hair so that the Indians could distinguish them from the Americans. Tecumseh evolved a strategy for the battle, which Muir accepted.

Where the road dipped down to run through a shallow valley, it was perfect country for Indian fighting. The road from Detroit to Monguaga, scarcely more than a trail wide enough for two wheels, lay in country rich in oak woods. Corn grew almost man-high in the cultivated fields.

Tecumseh planned to hide his Indians in a cornfield on

the American left. The Long Knife troops were to be allowed to pass the Indians, and once beyond them Muir would let them have it with a volley and a bayonet charge. The Indians would fall on their rear and trap them.

In the hot, Sunday summer afternoon of August 9, the advance guard of forty men under Captain Snelling came into the shade of the oak woods. Some sinister quality in the air affected the drummer boy. His music lost a beat or two and the men pricked up their ears. A nervous Indian could not restrain his hands and shot into the advancing left. Snelling instantly formed his men into a square. The Indians leapt as one man upon the enemy. But Snelling was a soldier, and managed his men and held his position. Miller would be with them in a moment, and Snelling would not run.

Tecumseh joined Muir, and the battle raged through the oak woods and along the banks of the river. The chief took a bullet in the fleshy part of his leg. Some of Tecumseh's men were mistaken by the British for Indians fighting on the American side, and they opened fire on them. The Indians replied in kind. For a while Indians and British fought each other with spirit, the sprigs of basswood notwithstanding. A group of seventy Indians under Billy Caldwell, bewildered by this sudden turn of events, fled from the fight. Muir ordered a bayonet charge just as a contingent of British Grenadiers arrived to support him. The bugler sounded the charge. The Grenadiers thought the order was being given for retreat and gave way without firing one single shot. They broke, and with Muir's own contingent retreated a quarter of a mile. Muir, wounded but on his feet, had trouble in rallying them again.

For a while Tecumseh alone was fighting with his remaining warriors. He put up a gallant stand with his fearsome fighters. The British seemed even more alarmed at the sounds of the horrendous Indian fighting, took to their boats, and fled to the Canadian shore.

The game was clearly to Miller, the American. But his cavalry officer became suddenly paralysed by fear. Captain Snelling ordered him out of the saddle and took command of the cavalry himself.

Tecumseh looked with admiration on this dashing, red-headed officer now leading his men. The chief put his braves under cover – suddenly there were no Indians to be seen. Captain Snelling wheeled his men about and withdrew to Monguaga. The Indians paddled their canoes back to Fort Malden.

Captain Brush's convoy was still motionless on the River Raisin.

9. Miracle at Detroit

THE British commander General Brock, Lieutenant-Governor of Upper Canada, quickly came to Fort Malden from York. He brought together his forces – regulars, militia, and volunteers – at Long Point. Three hundred men boarded small craft and bateaux, and struck through storm and heavy seas along the north shore of Lake Erie. Five more days of exhausting travel brought them to Amherstburg.

The Indians on Bois Blanc, whose eyes missed no movement of land or water, saw the ragged little fleet approach. A volley of musketry welcomed the British leader ashore. But Brock's first order was to still the guns. Ammunition was too scarce to waste on a welcome, even for the commanding officer himself.

Brock informed the senior officers of the garrison that he would see them in an hour. Within that hour he read the dispatches Tecumseh had taken from Van Horne at the Brownstown engagement. He concluded from his reading that American morale was very low indeed. This army that confronted him across the river in Detroit was a decidedly dispirited body of men. Could he attack Detroit at once?

The taking of Mackinac had provided a cheering moment. Until then most of the people of the province had scarcely dared to believe that there was hope in any shape for them in the face of American invasion. The Indians, as always impressed with victory, were fully ready to support the British now. If the Canadians could see Detroit snatched from American hands their confidence would strengthen immeasurably. Brock knew long before he reached Amherstburg that the Canadian position was very poor. The little country was facing a giant. What could possibly come of it? Brock wrote to the adjutant general, ". . . a full belief possesses the people that this province must inevitably succumb. This prepossession is fatal to every exertion. . . . I therefore must speak loud and look big. . . ."

He was facing Detroit now, and this was the moment for speaking loud and looking big.

In the evening of the day of Brock's arrival at Amherstburg Tecumseh called upon him. He brought a party of chiefs with him, and the commanders met with appropriate ceremony. The Shawnee was still limping from his wound. The Indian commissioner, Colonel Elliott, introduced the chief.

"This, sir," said Elliott, "is the Shawnee chief Tecumseh, who desires to be presented to you."

Tecumseh gave the British commander a shrewd appraisal. This was the man upon whom the whole future of the Indian race in North America might depend. He saw a man six feet three inches in height, broad and muscular. He had deep blue eyes and curly, butter-coloured hair. Candour and strength showed in his face. Brock was splendid in scarlet coat, white breeches, and gleaming, tall riding-boots, and his cocked hat lay on the table beside him. No detail escaped the chief's observant eye. Brock looked at Tecumseh with a frank and friendly gaze.

He saw a trim, spare, handsome Indian, slighter and shorter than himself, bearing himself with a quiet confidence. The chief was unobtrusively dressed, leaving as always the gay decoration and the bright blanket to lesser men. His well-cut buckskins were new and fresh, the silver gorget his only ornament. An eagle feather was thrust through his hair. He smiled, now, with complete and quiet satisfaction. He turned to his attending chiefs. "This is a man."

Tecumseh at that moment gave his full trust to the white commander. Brock extended his hand and Tecumseh grasped.

The British officers came in and the conference began. Brock gathered opinion on the practicability of making an attempt on Detroit. Colonel Procter vigorously protested such a foolhardy scheme. He pointed out that there were barely seven hundred men in the British forces, less than half of them regular soldiers. It would be the first fight for most of the militia who made up the rest of the army. They were poorly equipped. Procter discounted the value of the Indian fighters.

Detroit was a strong fort, well overhauled the year before. It had a twenty-foot parapet twelve feet thick at the top. The Americans had at least thirty-six big guns and quantities of ammunition. There were twenty-five hundred men in Detroit and the dispatches that the Indian Tecumseh had captured indicated that reinforcements were on the way from Ohio.

Procter sat down, glancing with distrust and uncomfortable concern at Tecumseh. He had not liked the look on the chief's face while he spoke of his lack of confidence in the Indian. More than once the Shawnee had shown Procter the way of valour. The British officer had little love for the Indian.

All officers but one agreed with Procter. The fiery quarter-

master Lieutenant-Colonel Nichols was for getting on with it without delay. He thought they could depend on the low morale of the Americans, fretting under the cowardice of their general.

Brock listened gravely. Then he said, as he nodded to Tecumseh, "Perhaps you would give us your opinion?" Tecumseh knew the terrain better than any British officer. He considered for a moment.

"It is possible to defeat the Long Knives. We remember Brownstown. We remember Monguaga."

The chief signed for one of his men to bring him a piece of bark. They unrolled it on the floor, and with his scalping-knife Tecumseh traced a map of the Detroit area, complete with streams, trails, rises and valleys, weak spots in the defences and strong. Shining black head with its flashing eagle feather and bright Anglo-Saxon head bent over the map in equal concentration.

Then Brock rose. "Gentlemen, we shall cross the river. We gain nothing by delay. We are committed to a war in which the enemy must *always* be our superior in numbers and ammunition."

It was four o'clock in the morning when the council ended. The chiefs were commanded to appear again with their warriors before Brock on the same day at noon.

Perhaps a thousand warriors faced the commander and his officers in the noonday sun. Ottawa, Chippewa, Wyandot, Potawatomi, Miami and Shawnee, Sauk and Fox, Kickapoo and Winnebago sat in a semicircle in a forest clearing.

Brilliant in white breeches and scarlet coats the British flanked Brock under the great Amherstburg oak. A ceremonial pipe passed among the chiefs and the officers. Then Brock rose and spoke formally to the Indians. His words reached their childlike, impressionable hearts.

He told them, with an intuitive understanding of the Indian mind, that he knew that the Americans were trying to drive the Indians from their lands, and that they were also invading British lands and meant to capture them too. Now, Indian and British together, they would cross the river and recapture their lands. The grave faces of the chiefs broke from their mask-like immobility and there were grunts of approval. Then Tecumseh spoke.

"We are happy that the father beyond the great salt water has at length awakened from his long sleep and permitted his warriors to come to the assistance of his red children. . . . The Americans are our enemies. . . . We gave them forest-clad mountains and valleys full of game, and in return what did they give our warriors and our women? Rum, trinkets and a grave."

He reminded his audience of Tippecanoe. Those brothers of theirs slaughtered at the Prophet's Town would find no rest in the hunting-grounds of the dead until their death had been avenged. The tribes must remain united, must fight side by side, until their enemies had been laid under the earth.

When he had finished, Roundhead, chief of the Wyandot, rose. Tecumseh, he said, had spoken for all the red men. When the great commander Brock had taken the hand of Tecumseh he had shaken the hands of a thousand Indians. The council was over.

Indians, British regulars, and Canadian militia, with Brock commanding, left Amherstburg for Sandwich very little more than twelve hours after Brock had arrived.

The silence of the little town of Sandwich, so lately evacuated by the Americans, was brusquely broken now. Three miles to the north of it, behind the underbrush in a grove of oak, the Royal Engineers constructed a battery. Five guns would point their noses straight towards Fort Detroit. Brock took up his headquarters in the great Georgian house that the fur-trader Jacques Bâby had built for himself. It was barely cold from being occupied by General Hull, whose headquarters it had been. Here Brock wrote a letter to Hull.

Headquarters, Sandwich, August 15, 1813

Sir,

The force at my disposal authorizes me to require of you the immediate surrender of Fort Detroit. It is far from my intention to join in a war of extermination, but you must be aware, that the numerous body of Indians who have attached themselves to my troops, will be beyond control the moment the contest commences. You will find me disposed to enter into such conditions as will satisfy the most scrupulous sense of honour. Lieutenant Colonel M'Donnell and Major Glegg are fully authorized to conclude any arrangement that may lead to prevent the unnecessary effusion of blood.

The officers named bore the letter under the flag of truce to General Hull, and returned with his answer. General Hull was prepared, he said, to meet any forces which General Brock had at his disposal. So the oaks were cut and the brush cleared in front of the guns, and the guns spoke. But they did not find their range or mark.

In the evening, sheltered by the darkness friendly to Indians, six hundred warriors under Tecumseh slipped down to the waterfront south of Sandwich.

At the council in Fort Wayne when Tecumseh broke the peace-pipe and accepted the British hatchet, he had commanded his braves to let no drop of whisky pass their lips until the Americans were humbled. They had had to agree.

And now, although they were on their way to fight the Americans, and perhaps in an hour their blood would flow, there was to be no torture, no punishment. The hated Americans were to be protected from harm if taken prisoner. Curious promises such as these he asked of them. When his warriors looked into the face of their commander, they could read in his eyes and in the stern gravity of his face the fate of any who should disobey.

Brock had asked of Tecumseh that there should be no barbarities after the fighting. "Where I am," said Tecumseh, "there is no atrocity."

Holding this strangeness in their minds, the Indians pulled their canoes softly out of the water. Wild-turkey calls, the monotonous song of the whippoorwill, and the melancholy yelp of the coyote sounded through the darkness about Detroit, as Indian tribe joined Indian tribe to surround the fort.

Across the river in Sandwich, Brock considered his strategy. He had memorized Tecumseh's map. The lie of the land was clear to him now. And this was his moment for talking and looking big. He must employ every ruse, too, to frighten that already nervous man commanding in Detroit. He must win this engagement. The safety, the future of Upper Canada, perhaps of British North America, might hang on his proving himself right. And, doubly, he must win because his officers did not think he could.

Brock sent a man with a fictitious dispatch in his pocket out to where he must certainly be captured. He was taken to the American side and searched. The dispatch on his person revealed that five thousand Indians were on their way from the upper lakes to join in the attack on Detroit.

Brock looked at the scarlet and white of his handsome

41st Regiment and thought it a very great pity that the militia could not be just as imposing. He found that a large number of cast-off red coats and white trousers could be provided for the first rank of men. The militia were made glorious in these. From across the river it would seem that the regular force was twice its actual size.

At sunrise the guns found their range, and were but feebly answered by the enemy. Boats and scows waited on the shore, and the troops with the newly uniformed militia clambered aboard. Sandwich rivermen stood ready to row the troops a mile across to the American side at Spring Wells, four miles below Detroit. The *Queen Charlotte*, her flags flying, stood by as a symbol of hope to the little flotilla, which moved off now towards an enemy country, towards an enemy at least three times its number and with many times its equipment for battle.

Tecumseh, mounted on his grey mustang, watched from a mound in an Indian burial-ground. He saw the unmistakable figure of the radiant British commander in the foremost boat, binoculars in hand. Among the first to land, Brock mounted a tall grey horse and, with Tecumseh on his mustang, reconnoitred his position.

Four miles along the Spring Wells road, the enemy lay in wait, his guns primed for action, his troops ready and eager to fight. At any moment there might be fire, in instant reaction to the temerity of their invasion. But although the guns at Sandwich still fired, the guns on the Spring Wells road were still.

The tough, wiry mustang and the shining war-horse carried their riders at the head of the invading army up along the narrow road. Tecumseh, slight and arrow-straight, dressed as always in the neatest and most inconspicuous buckskin, sat his horse as if he had been born with it. Brock, blazing in scarlet and white and brass, stood out like some too-flamboyant flower at the head of his men.

Nichols, the brave officer who, alone among the British, had approved the mad scheme to take Detroit galloped up to him, saluting. "Sir," he said, "you make too good a target here. Let me ride before you. If we lose you, we lose all." But Brock said, and Tecumseh noted it well, "I will not ask my troops to go where I cannot lead them."

The leaders drew their horses up for a moment, searching the land and trying to guess the moment when the attack might come. Tecumseh saw, a mile or so back on the road they had travelled, a wisp of moving dust. He signalled to Brock and they waited while the dust took the shape of a horse and rider. An Indian scout galloped furiously up to the chief. He spoke a few rapid words in the Shawnee tongue. Tecumseh nodded and translated the message for the British commander.

"McArthur the American is only three miles behind us."

"We move on Detroit immediately," Brock replied.

Over on the Canadian shore the people were gathered now in the little church of St. Ann's, and the quavering voice of the old rector prayed for victory for the King's forces, defeat to their enemies, and safe return for the men who had gone across the water. Voices rose in hymn and prayer through the soft, sunny air, punctuated always by the sound of the guns.

The shells were bursting in Detroit now, in the fort itself. Almost all of Hull's soldiers but the battery command on the Spring Wells road were crouching, by order of their general, in the fort at Detroit.

Indian war-whoops sounded wildly through the woods. Tecumseh's men passed in column three times out into the open view of the fort. Hull saw three times as many Indians as Tecumseh led, and the fearful shrieks of the Indians in the woodlands sounded in his terrified ears like the voices of the five thousand warriors expected from the Mackinac country.

Now the British could see the guns mounted on the Spring Wells road. At any moment they must fire, and how could they miss? The scarlet and white moving column on the narrow road made a perfect target. Were they being led into a trap by the silence of the guns?

The little army was within a quarter of a mile of the fort when the order came to swerve, and they moved to the left, halting about three hundred yards from the road. Apple trees heavy with fruit became a canopy above them. The Indian whoops were stilled for the moment. And all was silent on the American side.

The matches were lit for the Spring Wells guns, and the men stood ready to fire them. But the order was never given. Tecumseh and Brock, with M'Donnell and Glegg, leaving their men in the shelter and safety of the orchard, trotted to the top of a little knoll to see what was happening at the fort.

A shell from the Sandwich guns shot through an embrasure in the fort at Detroit and killed four officers. Hull was shrivelled with fear. He ordered his men not to fire at the approaching British. He sent a flag of truce to Sandwich, with proposals to confer on the terms of surrender.

Captain Dixon, in command of the guns at Sandwich, sent the messengers back. Brock was the man to decide what demands would be made. As Brock and Tecumseh rode along the Spring Wells road towards the top of their hill, their astonished eyes saw a gate open in the fort and an officer come out. He carried the white flag of surrender.

Colonel M'Donnell and Major Glegg met the officer. They returned at the gallop with the flag. Glegg pulled his horse back on its haunches and saluted.

"A flag, sir, from General Hull, proposing negotiations for the surrender of Detroit."

So the Stars and Stripes came down and the Union Jack went up over the fort. The defenders who had not been allowed to fight for their country stood by in shame.

Guns captured from the enemy cracked out the salute of victory. The *Queen Charlotte* sailed past the fort with flags and streamers flying, and answered the salute. In the evening the news of the fall of the fort reached Indian camps through the Michigan Territory by the swift Indian telegraph. Old warriors and women and children sang to the glory of the British and the Indians, and danced their victory dance.

Tecumseh and Brock congratulated each other, and exchanged gifts in token of their victorious collaboration. Brock took off his silk sash and threw it over the chief's shoulders. He presented him with a pair of handsome silver-mounted pistols. Tecumseh gave Brock his arrow-patterned sash, which Brock wore with pride. But it was Roundhead and not Tecumseh who wore Brock's gift. In Tecumseh's mind, Roundhead, chief of the Wyandot, was a more fitting recipient of the silken sash.

The town went mad when the British marched in. British officers kissed the guns which were now theirs, and which had once been captured from British forces. Indians rode horses, commandeered from the residents, breakneck through the streets. There was whooping and shouting and firing of guns in celebration. But no American head felt the tomahawk, no house the torch.

In the bell towers of St. Ann's little church across the river, a joyful peal rang out for victory.

Hull handed over the riches of his fort with an open, almost an eager, hand: thirty-three cannon, quantities of ammunition, a ship in the river, and 2,500 soldiers as prisoners of war. He included the forces of McArthur and Cass down by the Raisin. Their fury was unbounded at the news that they were to be part of the booty. Captain Brush's celebrated convoy, still beyond the river, was surrendered, at least on paper. But when Captain Elliott, son of the Indian agent, appeared before Captain Brush and ordered him to surrender his command, it was too much for that over-exasperated man. He threw Elliott into the guardhouse, harnessed his horses, yoked his oxen, and left for Ohio. Elliott was furious. He had come as an envoy and been treated as a criminal. He sent for Tecumseh. The chief swept down to the river with a party of Indians, but Brush was well on his way to Ohio then, and the Shawnee went back to Detroit.

Here passed a few of the strangest days in Tecumseh's life. He lived in a house, briefly sharing it with Brock. The great chief walked strangely regarded on the streets of Detroit. The newly-built little city was filled with prisoners of war, and among them there were many of Tecumseh's old friends and old enemies. They greeted him now with respect, many with admiration. General Brock wrote of him that "a more sagacious or more gallant warrior does not exist".

Tecumseh saw to the transfer of his Indians back to Malden. He gloried in the sight of the British flag over Detroit, and remembered that it floated over Mackinac too. He began to feel that the realization of an Indian country on the North American continent, free for ever from the encroachments of the Americans, was a reasonable expectation.

The Shawnee chief claimed, as his prize, a great farm where a thousand horses grazed, on the River Rouge. Here and on the streets of Detroit near by, elegant as always, with his silver-mounted tomahawk, his brace of pistols, and a buckskin mantle thrown over his shoulders, Tecumseh briefly rested in the peace and glory of victory.

Then Brock was off to the Niagara region. The Americans were stunned and shocked by these two victories, but they would recover, and Niagara was the likely route for their next invasion. The great commander was gone, the fort being left under the command of Major-General Procter. At no moment had Procter and Tecumseh any confidence in each other.

The new British general could accept no Indian on anything like equality. He was immeasurably disdainful of all fighting troops but British regulars. Tecumseh looked in Procter's fat face, where his little nose had all but disappeared in the cushion of flesh, to find nobility and courage. But the man of whom one American army officer wrote that he was "one of the meanest looking men I ever saw" offered neither of these aspects to his Shawnee ally.

Time and again Tecumseh forced the commander's hand – to find justice for a French priest who could not take an oath of allegiance to the British because he had already taken an oath of American allegiance, to insist on equal rations for Indian fighters and for British, and to follow with exasperated reluctance the chief's plans for battle. Tecumseh grew to hate and distrust Procter; Procter loathed Tecumseh and feared him. The Shawnee had, he saw, an almost miraculous influence over the Indians, and Procter distrusted and undervalued all Indians.

With Procter in command, the glory of Mackinac and Detroit faded. And then terrible news came from Brock himself to Procter, and from him to Tecumseh. It seemed that there was an armistice between the British and the Americans. They were not really at war at all. The armistice had been signed weeks before the taking of Detroit, but the news had not come through to the west.

This put Tecumseh in a dilemma. He and his Indians were for war to the death – continuous, bloody battling until the Americans were pushed back, to the sea itself, if possible, and the land freed for its rightful owners. Of what use would the brilliant victory at Detroit be in encouragement to the tribes if they learned that there was no war after all?

Tecumseh pondered on the strange way of the white man, who fought and did not fight his war. The Indian's mind refused to contain the thought that the fighting was over. But he could not fight alone in the north when his white allies told him there was peace now.

The message of the great victories had gone triumphantly south and east. The year before, Tecumseh had carried promises and hopes to the Creek, his mother's people. Now he could carry a tale of victorious accomplishment. He decided to go south again, and do what he could to enlist the southern tribes to his purposes.

The Shawnee rose from his meditations and gathered a little group of his best men about him. From the farm of a thousand horses they picked out fast black ponies, sturdy and beautiful. They set out for the country of the Creek.

Strange and sinister stories of this last, vast journey came out of the south as Tecumseh and his band flashed from Indian village to Indian encampment, telling their tales of triumph and of hate.

Legends grew out of a midnight meeting to which no

white man was admitted. Only scraps of sentences, blazing phrases, a few images remain from the fervent speech Tecumseh made that night. But when he had finished, the chiefs of the Creek rose as one man, except Old Warrior who loved the whites, and swore vengeance on the Americans. They swept Old Warrior from his command and raised young Weatherford – "Red Eagle" – in his place. Weatherford would grasp the hatchet in their name from the northern tribes.

Tecumseh's oratory lit fires of hate that were never quenched until thousands of Americans were slaughtered by Creek tomahawks and scalping-knives. Tecumseh's unusual humanity to prisoners could never have permitted the ghastly massacres, the indiscriminate killings, women and children as well as men, that the Creek perpetrated. But it was the Shawnee's voice they heard when they crept through the night to the slaughter. The bloody Creek war still raged long after the mighty warrior who instigated it had been carried to the wigwams of the dead.

The work done, Tecumseh's black horses cantered north again. Fresh fighters joined the band as the warriors rode along the Ohio and the Wabash until the Indians under Tecumseh who arrived at Fort Malden in April numbered six hundred. Counting all the Indians there and on Bois Blanc, there were perhaps three thousand. It is thought that this was the largest Indian force ever to gather anywhere, at any time, ready for fighting. And now Tecumseh knew that the war was at fighting heat, and had been for a long time, while he had been away.

When they had left the beautiful Bois Blanc island the birch leaves were turning to gold, and soon would leave the trees bare. Now the snow had come and gone, and the small leaves budded. Hope sprang in Tecumseh's heart as he came again to the land of the famous victory.

The British situation had changed as radically as the weather. The great commander, Brock, whose confidence and courage had given heart to an all but hopeless people, was dead.

As Brock had thought they would, the Americans had rushed into Canada through Niagara. The tall, scarlet-coated figure of the leader, unmistakable at the head of his soldiers, was shot down at the battle of Queenston Heights in October.

Perhaps the change that was most devastating to Tecumseh was that the leadership of the British in the west lay now in the plump hands of Major-General Procter.

The ignominious surrender of Detroit had raised American anger to boiling-point. Kentucky was particularly humiliated. Hull's name was reviled by men and children; women in knitting-parties snarled at the thought of him. The violent men of Kentucky swore revenge.

Harrison, Tecumseh's old adversary, was made supreme commander in the west. An eager detachment of Kentucky troops under General Winchester moved against the British and their Indian allies. They forced the British garrison at Frenchtown to withdraw to Brownstown. The Kentuckians camped at Frenchtown on the River Raisin. In the deep snows of a January night Procter, with 500 British and Canadians, and Roundhead with 450 Indians attacked Winchester's camp, and killed or captured his entire command of 850 men. Sixty-four Americans, wounded and helpless, were left waiting until their captors could send sleighs for them. Procter promised them protection in surrender. A band of Indians, drunk with victory and whisky and quite beyond Roundhead's control, scalped the wounded men as they lay in the snow.

The Americans were enraged. Troops from Kentucky and Ohio, distrusting each other but joining in hating the Indians, were offered to Harrison. The government issued no uniforms for them. In coonskin hats, bell-crowned hats, buckskin pants, homespun suits, brown shirts, and yellow shirts, no two men alike, they joined to fight Tecumseh. For the outrage was blamed on him. His was the Indian name that everyone knew.

"Remember the River Raisin" became the battle cry of the Kentuckians. It was hurled to inspire the enemies of Tecumseh, although the Shawnee chief had been a thousand miles away from Frenchtown at the time of the massacre.

10. Bugles on the Maumee

THE fury of the Kentuckians at the news of the taking of Detroit had brought them bloodthirsty to the army. But instead of marching on Detroit, Harrison built Fort Meigs, up-river from Fort Miami. Here he would stay until the right moment came to try for Detroit. Defrauded of their battle, many of his forces deserted. Procter laid plans to take Fort Meigs before any move on Detroit could be made. Tecumseh and his Indians were wild to be fighting. Activity had to be provided for the Indians, as for the Kentuckians, to keep them from slipping away.

The strong core of Tecumseh's forces were Sioux and Chippewa, who would fight under no other leader. For the movement on Harrison at Fort Meigs, Tecumseh had about 1,200 warriors. Procter could muster nine hundred men – British regulars and Canadian militia.

Harrison sat in Fort Meigs on the south side of the Maumee River, making plans and fervently hoping that General Green Clay with his three regiments, said to be coming up the Maumee, would hurry. On an April day the outposts at Fort Meigs looked across the river and saw two riders, magnificently mounted, evidently reconnoitring. They jumped to the conclusion that the riders were Procter and Tecumseh. Their guns tore up the ground at the horses' feet. The pair disappeared unharmed into the woods, but now in the forests on both sides of the river hundreds of Indians roamed.

Procter transferred his troops via Lake Erie to the mouth of the Maumee; then, by small vessels and by open boats, British regulars and Canadian militiamen moved up the river. Old Fort Miami was friendly again to the Indians' cause. They came to the fort overland.

Procter constructed batteries on the north side of the river across from Fort Meigs and bombarded the fort heavily. On May the first he demanded the surrender of the fort. But the fearful cries of a thousand Indians reverberated in Kentucky ears. As long as the fort held, American soldiers had no desire to submit themselves to the River Raisin treatment. Clay would soon be coming. Harrison answered the demand for surrender with contempt. Tecumseh tried to taunt Harrison into a fight. "Come out and give me battle – you hide behind logs and in the earth like a ground-hog," was the message the chief sent the general. But the American was not to be moved. Roman generals counselled discretion before valour.

Tecumseh commanded the Indian forces, the Wyandot Walk-in-the-Water and Splitlog supporting him. They threw the bulk of the Indian fighters across the Maumee, and sealed the approaches to Fort Meigs with scouts. General Clay sent a little advance party to Harrison, asking for orders. Tecumseh captured the party. Harrison walked the floor, waiting for news. None came. Finally one of his lieutenants, under cover of darkness and disguise, slipped through the Indian patrols. Clay got his orders.

He was to split his forces. The larger party, under Dudley, must land on the north bank of the Maumee opposite Fort Meigs. This force must capture the British batteries, spike the cannon, dash back to their boats, and cross the Maumee to the American fort. In the meantime Clay was to land on the south bank and Harrison would march out to meet him. Together they would beat off Tecumseh's main body of warriors, move into the fort, and unite with Dudley.

It was a fine plan but it did not reckon with Tecumseh's gift for on-the-spot strategy. The chief offered small resistance to Clay's little army as it made its way into the fort. This was not the main issue. The successful beginning of his plan Harrison saw from across the river. Dudley spiked the guns. The British flag went down over the battery, the American flag went up. Then Harrison lost sight of his north-bank army.

Dudley's left companies, not engaged in spiking the British cannon, were attacked by a detachment of Tecumseh's Indians. The gun-spikers heard heavy firing in the woods. They rushed to help their compatriots. The Americans, united, triumphantly pushed the Indians through the bush, over fallen trees and streams in freshet, until they had gone two miles from the river and the fort. Procter, seeing Indians pursued, quickly sent word to Tecumseh. Procter was now bringing his troops in to Dudley's right. Tecumseh took his men to the river below the fort. In boats, or fording or plunging in and swimming, the Indians took up their position in the rear of Dudley's entire force. There was sudden music from British bugles. The Indians who had been chased turned and faced the Kentucky force. Then Dudley saw what had happened. Indians in front, Indians behind, British soldiers to the right, between him and the river. The men from Kentucky were trapped like rats in a hole.

Those who could run, ran. Those who could not escape,

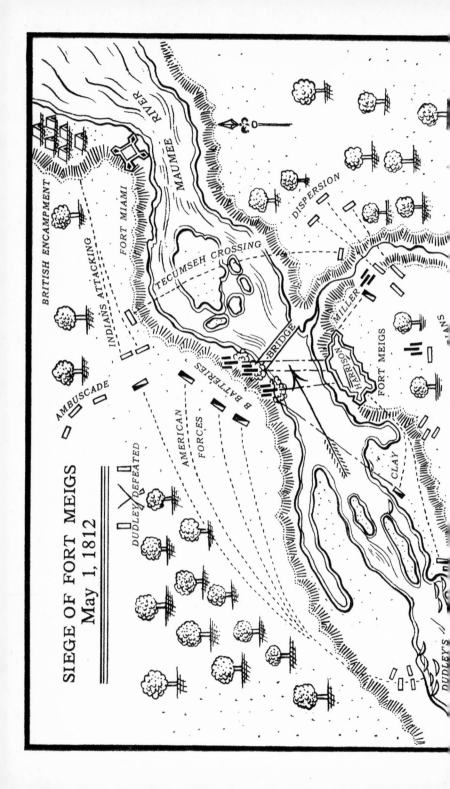

SIEGE OF FORT MEIGS
May 1, 1812

and there were hundreds of these, were shot down. Harrison sent a courier with an order to retreat, but there was no place for retreat. Dudley, a big-boned, fat man "not built for running", was killed and scalped. It was every Kentuckian for himself, in terrible confusion. The officers tried to re-form when they came again to the batteries. But the batteries had been recovered by the British when Dudley left them to chase Indians. Few lived to gain the river. Four hundred and eighty men were killed, and one hundred and fifty captured.

Tecumseh, joyful with his victory over Dudley, went over the river to see what could now be done about Harrison. The prisoners were marched under guard of British soldiers to Fort Miami. Here the Indians, free from Tecumseh's presence and command, forgot all that he had taught them. Once again the shameful gauntlet was run, a fearful mani-festation of the Indian lust for blood and the torture of prisoners. The warriors, wild with excitement, lined up on either side of the road to the fort, and the desperate prisoners passed through a barrage of gun-stocks, tomahawks, and scalping-knives in their rush to the gates of the fort. At least twenty were killed and thrown into the ditch before they reached the gate. Once inside it was no better. The British guard were totally unable to control the blood-fired Indians. Tomahawks and guns were turned on the prisoners. Scalps were sliced, torn, and ripped from heads, and the hideous laughter of the victorious savage filled the guardroom. No order came from Procter to stop the outrage. A tall, heavy Indian came to the centre of the terrified group. He took a butcher knife, and, passing his finger along the edge, looked to see which victim would be his first. Then there was a roar and a rush outside the gate. Tecumseh entered the fort at a gallop. A sudden, stricken silence fell over the place. Tecumseh's voice thundered out, "Are there no men here?"

An Indian was holding a tomahawk over a prisoner, the victim mesmerized with fear. The Indian's arm seemed frozen. Tecumseh felled him with a stroke of his sword. He jumped from his horse and caught a warrior by the throat, hurling him to the ground. His Indians slunk from him like beaten dogs.

Alone, Tecumseh walked slowly to find Procter. His shoulders drooped. For this moment it seemed to him that all the striving, all the journeyings, all the teaching for all the years had been in vain. He had taught his people nothing. Almost within his presence they had massacred helpless men. Victory was nothing to them unless there was booty, torture, and revenge. There was no humanity in them. He suffered as the greatest suffer when they see their disciples fail. He had not raised his Indians one step above their primitive savagery.

"Oh, my poor Indians, my poor Indians, what will become of them?"

His steps became slower as he neared Procter's quarters. Where was Procter? Why had he not protected his prisoners? Why had he not protected the Indians from themselves and his prisoners from these savage children?

Tecumseh's anger rose. He found Procter and demanded an explanation. "Your Indians," Procter said coldly, "cannot be controlled." Tecumseh looked at the pudgy face and the double chin offering only weakness. He himself had quelled the Indians in seconds. He gave the British officer the greatest of Indian insults. He said, "You should go and put on petticoats. You are a woman. You are unfit to command." Procter said nothing.

The British forces desperately needed strong reinforcements. Procter wrote sheaves of letters to Sir George Prevost, Commander-in-Chief, asking for men, men, more men. He did not get them, or he got them in such little parties that he could, he said, do little that was effective with them. Had he got the men, instead of promises of men, he could have done wonders on land and on lake. One great advantage would have been that he needn't then have had to depend upon Indians, whom he had always deeply distrusted. He knew, too, with a puzzled acknowledgement, that these creatures held him, a British officer, in some kind of strange, savage contempt.

The contempt increased. Although at Fort Meigs all those scores of prisoners had been taken, and all those hundreds of Kentuckians killed, still after days and days of trying, Procter's guns had not been able to take the fort. He had tried again in July, and again had not succeeded. When, largely to win Tecumseh's good opinion, he had led a force against Fort Stephenson and failed there too, his reputation had reached a very low level indeed. British arms were a grave disappointment to the Indians.

Tecumseh had become a very sore thorn in the Procter flesh. He had a way of taking the initiative that infuriated the general.

There was the case of the horse-meat. Procter's plump face reddened when he thought of that encounter. It had come to Tecumseh's sharp ears that his Indians were being rationed with horse-meat, while the British troops ate beef. He strode into Procter's quarters and taxed him with the story. The interview was a short one. Tecumseh struck Procter's sword with the flat of his hand and lightly stroked his own tomahawk. "You are Procter," he said; "I am Tecumseh." No invitation to a duel was ever more clearly given. The Indians got their beef.

But, like it or not, Procter must make do with Tecumseh and his men. More than a thousand Indians, all in perfect condition, were at Fort Malden and on Bois Blanc in the summer of 1813. They had little to do and grew restless.

The British could see that the next action would be on water, not land. Procter wrote again to the Commander, begging for men. A hundred and fifty sailors, he said, would have prevented a ruinous landing of the enemy at Long Point on the provision route. The flow of goods to Amherstburg was being interfered with now, by enemy action. "I must entreat your Excellency to send me more troops – I apprehend the enemy's rapid advance to the River Raisin in force —"

Well might Procter fear. In the early days of the war the American government had thought that it would be necessary to do no more than march through the Canadas, and the British flag would come down. Defeat after defeat had been inflicted on their troops and the Americans were now aroused. The old and incompetent generals of the early days had been replaced by determined and brave ones. Harrison in Fort Meigs was no General Hull. Procter knew that Harrison was meditating upon strong reprisals. But he did not move. What was he waiting for?

The Americans had learned, and learned well, the lesson of Captain Brush's convoy that never came in. Whoever controlled Lake Erie could control the west. There must be warships on the lake capable of supplying the forts. Until Lake Erie was cleared of the British patrol, there was no point in trying to retake Detroit.

The Americans set up a shipyard at Erie (Presqu'Ile). Two ships took shape there, and while the light lasted the yards rang with the sounds of the shipwright's hammer.

The Indians watched without understanding. Why were the enemy building ships instead of fighting?

The Americans built fast at Erie.

By late summer they were ready to fight for the lake.

The Canadian shores produced little but timber for the building of ships. Guns, cables, anchors, and cannon must all be brought from Britain. Only the great ropes could be made from Upper Canadian hemp. Even the builders for the tiny shipyard at Amherstburg had to come from Britain.

And the enemy was being watchful now, on the provision line to Amherstburg. Fifty thousand dollars' worth of "cables, cordage, canvas, tools and stores of every kind" addressed to Niagara and Malden was burned during the successful American attack on York.

A British sailor, Captain Barclay, who had lost one arm at Trafalgar, now took over the British fleet on Lake Erie. The darling of the fleet, the beautiful 19-gun brig *Detroit*, was still on the stocks when Barclay took over. The Indians watched the building of the "great canoe" with interest and bewilderment.

Procter, jittery and frenzied, sent the *Detroit* out, Barclay in command, to engage the Americans when the brig was barely launched. She never did get her own guns. Cannons were rooted up from Malden and set on her decks. Sails were snatched from the *Queen Charlotte* to furnish her.

The Americans won the battle of Lake Erie. And so the precious advantage of the control of the lake slipped from the hands of the British. It was not lightly lost. "The heavy metal won the day in an action which was as valiantly and as bitterly contested as any ever fought on fresh water or salt."

Harrison was free now to load his men on ships, well armed and ready. Lake Erie lay free to any American craft. The way to Fort Malden was wide open to the Long Knives.

11. The Reluctant Retreat

Tecumseh and his Indians at Fort Malden and Bois Blanc saw the great canoe go out and heard the roar of the guns, but for a week afterwards knew nothing of the results of the battle. It was left to the chief to read the signs for himself.

There was unusual activity at Fort Malden. Procter seemed busy with baggage. Mutinous junior officers moved through the camp with quiet, sullen faces. Gradually Tecumseh realized the truth. The great one-armed British sailor had been defeated. Soon, undoubtedly, Harrison and the Long Knives would be across the river looking for battle. Why, then, were not Procter and his men and Tecumseh and his Indians making full and joyful preparations to meet them? But no preparations were being made. All was dullness and apathy on the north shore of Lake Erie.

On the 18th of September at a full council with Procter and his officers, Tecumseh heard what the British general had to say. The enemy had everything, Procter said – food, guns, unconquerable numbers. Food was short now on the British side. Barclay had taken much, and it was lost. The guns that were expected had not come. There was nothing they could do when they lacked so much. They must burn their forts, so that the enemy would find nothing. The British strategy would be to lead the Americans on far into British territory, to a place far from their ships, where many of the King's soldiers would join them. Then, he said, they might turn and defeat Harrison and his army.

Tecumseh leapt to his feet, his eyes burning in fury. Backed by his thousand Indians, he faced the quaking Procter and gave his response to the cowardly plan to run from Harrison.

"Father – listen! Our fleet has gone out; we know they have fought; we have heard the great guns; but know nothing of what has happened to our father with one arm. Our ships have gone one way and we are much astonished to see our father tying up everything and preparing to run away the other – we must compare our father's conduct to a fat animal that carries its tail upon its back, but when affrighted it drops it between its legs and runs off.

"Listen, father! The Americans have not yet defeated us by land; neither are we sure that they have done so by water; – you have got the arms and ammunition which our great father sent for his red children. If you have any idea of going away give them to us and you may go in welcome, for us. Our lives are in the hands of the Great Spirit. We are determined to defend our lands, and if it is his will we wish to leave our bones upon them."

The warriors leapt up, brandishing their tomahawks. Fierce yells reverberated through the hall of the council chamber. The chiefs were ready to kill the British now, if Tecumseh thought the moment was ripe. Procter left the meeting abruptly.

Tecumseh dismissed his people with a slight gesture. "I will see Procter," he said to his aides, "and find out what is in his mind. If Harrison comes, we must go to meet him." He called on Elliott, the Indian agent, and insisted that they should visit the general together.

Shamed before his officers, taught his duty by a savage, Procter was in no mood to see Tecumseh. He was almost as afraid to meet the Indian as he was to face Harrison, who was coming in overpowering strength. Perhaps five thousand men had boarded the American ships bound for Middle Sister Island on their way to the British shore. Fifteen hundred Long Knives left Fort Meigs at the same time, bound for Detroit. Procter saw Harrison's army as ten thousand sharp-shooting Kentuckians, all coming straight for General Procter to avenge the River Raisin. He had no stomach to fight. He wanted only to get on his way to Niagara, to the protection of the British troops there. His officers held him in deepening scorn.

And now Tecumseh stood on his doorstep and he was compelled to see him. A British general was reduced to explaining his plans to an Indian, a savage chief who stood there holding him in the most obvious contempt. Tecumseh thought with a falling of his heart how different it would have been if Brock, the rash, confident Brock, had led the British. Brock had said, "Come and fight the Americans!" Sometimes Procter said, "Go and fight the Americans!" But now he was saying, "Run, the Americans are coming!" Had Brock lived, he, Tecumseh, need not have had to come to this fat man's quarters to try to shame him into fighting.

The Indian subtly understood that Procter had all but washed his hands of the war. His mind was on his own safety, on his daughter who was ill, on the problems of transporting his wife to safety in the east, and on the urgent necessity of caring for his plentiful and handsome personal baggage.

Tecumseh's plan was simple and direct. The Americans were to be allowed to land and move towards Amherstburg and Fort Malden. Tecumseh would fall on the rear and flank of the army, and Procter would attack it in the front with his regular soldiers and militia. If the British and Indians were beaten back they would retire to their old stand at the Aux Canards River, where Tecumseh had held out before. If he were moved from there he would go to another favourable place. But he did not think he would be moved. His Indians were fresh and blazing to fight. Procter shook his head contemptuously.

"You are a miserable old squaw!" said Tecumseh, stroking his tomahawk. Procter blenched but dared not object to the epithet. There was danger in Tecumseh's fierce eyes, and death in the glitter of his ever-ready scalping-knife. The general was forced by fear and shame and the presence of the Indian agent to promise that he would fall back no farther than the Thames River. Chatham, Tecumseh said, would be the farthest point to which he could consent to go before meeting Harrison. Procter went safely from the interview. Perhaps he had lost his only chance of effectively resisting the American army.

The fort was set to the torch. Tecumseh felt his heart ever more heavy within him. "We are going to follow the British," he said to a warrior, "and I feel certain that we shall never return."

At Sandwich the fur-trader Jacques Bâby gave a dinner for the high-ranking officers of Procter's army, and Tecumseh. It was a gathering of nervous men. The Indian put his two pistols on either side of his plate, and his hunting-knife before it. In honour of the occasion he threw a scarlet cloak over his shoulders.

There was a knock at the door. The whole company jumped. A sergeant entered and announced that the Ameri-

can fleet had entered the Detroit River. It was sailing north now, under a light breeze. Tecumseh rose, put his hands on his pistols, and spoke directly to Procter with a quiet, fierce insistence.

"Father, we must go to the enemy and prevent him from coming here. We are quite numerous enough. I tell you I am sorry I have listened to you this far. We could have taken our stand behind the great sandbanks of Father Elliott's point. There, beyond any doubt, we could have kept the enemy from landing and held our hunting-grounds for our children. Now you want to withdraw to the River Thames – I am tired of it all! Every word you say blows to nothing like the smoke from our pipes. You are like the crawfish that does not know how to walk straight ahead."

Procter said nothing, dismissed the diners, packed up his goods, and left. The Americans were hot on his heels.

Tecumseh left scouts to give information on the movement of the American troops. Then he and his thousand remaining warriors followed the British eastward, starting that night. There was no choice for the Indians.

Up-stream to Chatham the strange, reluctant retreat began. Far in advance ran Procter, many of the military wagons loaded with his precious belongings. Wives and families and the sick travelled with the retreating army. Ammunition that should perhaps have travelled in the wagons went by bateaux. Tecumseh and his bewildered Indians brought up the rear. Not all the red men had come with the Shawnee chief. The strangeness of this war, the incomprehensibility of the effect that a battle between the great canoes could have on the people on land had discouraged many of the warriors. And this was strange country to many of them. They slipped away. But there still remained the faithful thousand.

The American Admiral Perry, who had beaten Barclay, pursued the retreating army by water. He stood by with his warships while the Indians left on guard at Detroit were driven out and the American flag was raised once more over Detroit. He crossed Lake St. Clair then, and took two small boats up the Thames. But Tecumseh had warriors stationed along the river bank. Perry's sailors were raked by fire. Perry left the water.

Tecumseh's men destroyed none of the bridges which the retreating army crossed, and which the pursuing army was soon to cross. Tecumseh begrudged every step he took away from his enemy. He left the way open for the Americans to reach him, when he might stand and fight.

Chatham, Procter had said. So at Chatham Tecumseh looked around and found a good spot for defence. There was already a blockhouse and a scattering of log cabins. McGregor's Creek joined the Thames here. Tecumseh looked at the marrying of the currents. "It reminds me," he said, "of the Tippecanoe and the Wabash."

Procter was now more than twenty miles away. Colonel Warburton was in command. "This is the place," Tecumseh said to the colonel. It was the first that Warburton had heard that the British were to halt here and fight the Americans. He gallantly agreed to honour Procter's pledge. The troops and Indians spent the night at Chatham, but in the morning before the men had time to cook their freshly killed meat for breakfast, news came that Harrison was close upon them. Warburton ordered an instant retreat.

Hungry, ill-equipped with the weapons of war, and abandoned by their general, the troops were in no condition for a fight. Warburton ordered a withdrawal to Moraviantown. The soldiers fired McGregor's mill and a stand of arms, and departed.

Tecumseh and his Indians fought for the Chatham bridge alone. A battery of six-pounders, a volley of grape-shot met the Indian fighters. Tecumseh was shot in the arm by a rifle ball but he kept on fighting. Thirteen of Tecumseh's men were killed, and many more wounded. Walk-in-the-Water, the wavering Wyandot, wavered for the last time. He defected from Tecumseh's army and with sixty of his warriors went over to the enemy. But Harrison sent him sharply back to Detroit.

It was clear to Tecumseh that his Indians could not fight cannon. His men were being battered with no hope of gain. He ordered them to move off to Arnold's mill at the rapids of the Thames twelve miles away. With the order to retreat came a stern command to fire no grist-mills. The destruction of the settlers' property had no bearing on the war, in Tecumseh's mind.

Realizing that the Americans were advancing swiftly, Tecumseh had made his way back to the British army by the time darkness fell.

The fleeing Procter had returned. Once his baggage, his wife, and his daughter were safe, he had taken up his command again. But there was little joy in the British camp. The men were hungry still, and terrible news had leaked through to the camp. Two bateaux with Procter's full reserve of ammunition and supplies had fallen into the enemy's hands. Most of the men had no more ammunition than lay in their pouches, and now there was no more. What hope did they have?

Harrison threw up careful entrenchments around his camp. In the evening Tecumseh inspected the layout. He decided that it would be a thoroughly feasible idea to attack by a night assault. Confusion, he knew, could easily result from night attack, swift and surprising. Procter refused point-blank – even to consider the suggestion.

There was nothing to do then but wait for the revealing light of day.

At last the time had come. Tomorrow Tecumseh and his old adversary Harrison must surely meet. Old friends and old enemies of many years' standing would face each other and fight before another sun had set.

The Indians were a mile and a half beyond the British camp. They sat in silence, which was common to an Indian meeting unless there was something of real importance to say. Their bivouac fire blazed comfortably in the centre of the circle.

Tecumseh looked in the faces of the men about him. There was Shabbona, faithful through many journeys, many years, and many throws of fate. His aide and friend Billy Caldwell, the Winnebagos Naw Kanw and Four Legs, and Wasegoboah, his sister's husband. These were the men who were faithful to him, faithful to the bone, following without question where he led. They asked for no better occupation, believing that there could be no more honourable one.

A heavy grief lay on Tecumseh's heart. Terrible news came from the south. The Creeks whom he had roused were massacring the Americans and torturing their women and children. And Red Eagle, whom he thought of as the man who would lead the Indians to their rightful heritage if he should die, had been utterly unable to restrain them. So

terrible had been the sight – a whole fort full of helpless prisoners in a bath of blood – that Weatherford could not stand to watch. His shrieking, bloodthirsty Indians slashed and slew and laughed like fiends. Weatherford leapt on his great black horse and rode away from the sight. Tecumseh knew what awful reprisals would come from this disaster. The Indian fate in the south was sealed. Tecumseh lifted his shoulders, and sighed in recognition of supreme failure. If Weatherford, whom he had admired and trusted, could do nothing with his people, what hope was there for them under lesser guidance? More immediately, what hope was there for him here tomorrow, what hope for the childlike people who could not look after themselves?

The Shawnee looked at the men about him. Faithful, yes, utterly faithful, but they were followers, not leaders. Tecumseh knew only too well the wavering Indian heart. There was no one here who could steady it.

Someone put more wood on the fire. It was cold, this night of October the fourth, in Upper Canada. The leaves were falling fast now, the crisp air telling of the winter to come. The sparks flew up, rushing towards the sky. Tecumseh watched them climb. Suddenly he gave a great, anguished cry. His friends gathered round him, afraid that a bullet from the surrounding darkness must have struck him. Across the darkness of the sky there lingered for a second longer the last brief glow from the swift passage of a shooting star.

"I shall die, tomorrow," Tecumseh said. The strange perception common to his family, which had told his father that he must die, the premonition that came to his brother Cheeseekau, came now to the leader of his people.

A wail, a lamentation went up from the men about the fire.

Tecumseh spoke to them, then. "Do not make my son a chief," he said; "there is too much white blood in the boy. He is too much like his mother." Then he sighed deeply. "Give him my sword, when he is man enough to carry it."

He chose no successor, gave no name to his faithful few. Who was there to choose?

The Indians sat a long time after that, silent about the fire, feeling the chill of death already in their hearts.

12. Moraviantown

AT DAYBREAK on the morning of October the fifth the British under Major Muir sent men into the fields to capture and kill cows for their breakfast. They lit great fires and cut up the carcasses for their breakfast barbecue. Word flashed up from the river that the Americans were coming. Procter, nervous and wary as a cat, ordered the companies to form. Once again the British were to march on empty stomachs. They marched five and a half miles to a spot where the road came close to the right bank of the Thames.

Procter need not have hurried. There was plenty of time for breakfast. Harrison, as sure of his prey as a fox in a henhouse, knew that he did not have to burn the road beneath his feet. He kept most of his force on the south side of the fast-running Thames until the early morning. Then he embarked his men in bateaux. Those for whom there was no room in the flat-bottomed boats held fast to the manes of the horses and crossed with the swimming beasts. By midmorning the American army was on the north side of the river, marching deliberately down the river road.

Procter's brief spurt of energy evaporated by noon. Its only result was to deprive the troops of their breakfast. Tecumseh, bringing back his aides from their advanced post in the morning, very nearly killed the British general, who

had lost all desire or competence for fighting. Tecumseh
demanded plans and orders from him. He got only fears and
subterfuge. Tecumseh raised his gun, ready to shoot. Elliott
threw up the barrel, and Procter was saved for a more in-
glorious destiny than being shot by the great Shawnee brave.
The memory of the River Raisin and his likely fate if the
Kentuckians found him obscured every other vision from the
general's mind.

Trembling with a double fear, Procter agreed to stand
where he was. Tecumseh laid out the plan of battle. The
British troops, knowing that their only ammunition now lay
in their pouches, hungry as hunters, having been compelled
to march all those miles without a bite of breakfast, were in
no mood to praise Procter. He didn't seem to have any idea
what to do with them. He marched them, he halted them.
He faced them the other way, changed his mind, and faced
them back again. One of them said that "they were ready to
fight for their knapsacks, wished to meet the enemy, but did
not like to be knocked about in that manner, doing neither
one thing nor the other."

They looked down the road they now faced and saw a
group of British soldiers without weapons running towards
them. They had escaped from the boats captured by the
Americans at Chatham. "Only a mile off!" they gasped,
"Harrison is coming!"

There was a single roadway to Moraviantown. Harrison
must come this way. As the British faced Harrison, a small
swamp lay on the right of the road, the river on the left.
Tecumseh planned to have the British span the roadway, a
first line and a reserve line. Procter would be in the reserve
line. On the far side of the small swamp, with the British
on their left, Tecumseh put half his Indians, under his com-

mand. He set himself the position of being as close as possible to Procter. It seemed to him that Procter might need encouragement, if not physical persuasion. Far to the right of Tecumseh, about three hundred yards away in a large swampy area, the chief established his Chippewa and Sioux under Oshawahnah, faithful to death. The braves from the Lake Superior area were among the strongest supports Tecumseh had. Great trees and heavy tangled undergrowth here would hide the braves from the enemy. The Indians knew that Harrison had more than twice as many available fighters as the British. But this was the kind of ground Indians liked for fighting. When Harrison, advancing on the road, came into the thick of the fight with the British, then the Indians under Oshawahnah would fall upon the American left.

Well satisfied that the arrangement of fighters was as good as could be made, Tecumseh reviewed the battle position. The certainty of a fight at last filled the Shawnee with elation. He strode to Procter, extending his hand, "Father! Have a big heart! Tell your young men to be firm, and all will be well." He might almost have been Procter's father himself, soothing his fractious child. The chief went down the main British line then, greeting old friends, shaking hands with each officer, putting heart into the hungry, despairing men, who knew that there was really no hope. Then he went back to the Indians, waiting in the woods. "Be brave," he commanded them, "stand firm, shoot straight."

Indian scouts brought word that Harrison was close at hand. Procter suddenly said, "Form up across the road!" It might have meant several things. The front line under Colonel Warburton's command stretched out between river and swamp. The men stood behind widely spaced trees. Their one six-pounder, capable of shooting only fifty yards, was placed on the centre of the first line, on the road. The soldiers formed themselves "in cluster and confusion".

It was four o'clock in the afternoon when the sound of bugles, American cavalry bugles, echoed through the woods. Harrison, the cautious Harrison, who had been taught by the Romans to be safe before he was great, utterly changed character at Moraviantown. Instead of putting his foot soldiers farther along the road he suddenly threw his cavalry against the British. "The measure was not sanctioned by anything I had seen or heard of, but I was fully convinced it would succeed. The American backwoodsmen ride better in the woods than any other people. A musket or rifle is no impediment." He was terribly right.

The bugle sounded and the cavalry charged. James Johnson and his yelling Kentucky riders crashed through the woods, their rifles blazing away at the little groups of standing redcoats, who were as undirected as shepherdless sheep. The first line of the British gave way at once with scarcely time to load their rifles until the horsemen were upon them. Procter did not wait to see more. With the dreaded cry "Remember the River Raisin" ringing in his ears the British general tore back to his waiting carriage and whipped up his horses. He rattled on his cowardly way to Burlington Heights, where his wife, his daughter, and his baggage waited for him. Americans in pursuit captured the carriage, but Procter escaped. Fifty of the British ran after their general. Six hundred remained, many without ammunition. With cavalry in front of them and rank after rank of American foot soldiers approaching, they had no choice but to surrender.

Oshawahnah had no chance to fall on Harrison's flank –

the infantry he had been directed to attack were diverted far from his stand. He could only wait.

The British accounted for, the whole attention of the Americans could now be directed to the Indians. There was a rush towards the chief's stand by the "Forlorn Hope", a swashbuckling band of old Indian-fighters. Riding furiously from the great swamp, they were shot from their saddles, their plunging horses left riderless. Oshawahnah raked the American left with a heavy fire, and drove the enemy back.

Colonel Johnson now began a systematic engagement against Tecumseh. His officers rode their mounts still, but his soldiers dismounted. Together they made a steady advance to the little swampy wood where Tecumseh and his men still stood. Tecumseh's great voice roared through the bush, "Attack! Attack! Attack!" One of the American raiders reported, "He yelled like a tiger, and urged his braves to attack. We were then but a few yards apart."

The Shawnee was everywhere at once. He had bound his head with a white silk handkerchief to keep the long black hair from his eyes. A jaunty ostrich feather rose above his brow, and about his wounded arm he still wore a bandage. His men were painted, streaked, and fearsome, mingling their scarlet and black and yellow paint with the colours of the falling leaves – the red of the maple, the brown of the beech. Blood from the white man and the red mingled its vermilion with the autumn brilliance.

Blood flowed from the great chief's mouth. Billy Caldwell, looking across from where he still fought with his Canadian comrades, called to him, "Are you wounded?" "I am shot," said Tecumseh, and staggered along the line, using his rifle as a crutch. Once more he roared – in the

Chippewa tongue to the Chippewa warriors – that they must stand firm and the victory was theirs.

Old Whiteley, leading the "Forlorn Hope", shot at what might have been an apparition of an Indian. But the apparition shot back, and both men fell dead. A youngster of nineteen, exalted by the sight of his first blood and battle, screamed to the air that he had killed "one damned yellow bugger". Colonel Johnson, wounded but battling still from

his horse, shot his remaining bullets into any redskin that wavered before him. There was indescribable confusion of bullet and blood. Gradually the bullets told, and the Indians moved back into the shelter of the swamp. Then, suddenly, the fighters realized that the great voice had ceased for ever to call courage to his men.

The fight was over, the Indian star had set. It was never to rise again in North America.

13. Where Lies Tecumseh?

No white man knows where Tecumseh lies. Those bowed bones, so long ago bent by a buffalo, have never been found, although many have searched. Where is the silver gorget which lay on that mighty chest? Where the noble head?

Foolish drifting stories came down from the battle of the Thames – this man or that had found the body of an Indian, richly dressed, certainly the body of a chief, certainly of Tecumseh. But the body of the great Shawnee chief was never richly dressed in life. No gaudy ribbons, no epaulets, no bracelets, no rings were there, ever, for him. His bones, wherever they rest, are wrapped in simple buckskin, fringed. There may be still, perhaps, a bandage about the arm which held a rifle ball at Chatham.

Even yet, a hundred years and half a century more since the greatest of all Indians fell for ever at Moraviantown, some man remembers that his grandfather or his grandfather's friend knew, and told him, where the Shawnee lay. Then there go modern men with picks and shovels, maps and instructions, out in expedition to dig and to find the place, to dig and find the bones. But they are never there. Carried away, the searchers say, by freshet or landslide. Or the tree is gone, which marked the grave.

The bones lie yet in some secret place. They are the bones of a man who died following his own, bright guiding star. He never wavered once in the stern duty he had set himself. He failed because it was not possible that he could succeed. But he never admitted the possibility of failure. He carried his dream, the dream for the salvation of his people, to the very last moment of his majestic life.

Perhaps it is right that the white men do not know where Tecumseh lies buried. They had stripped his people of their country. They had failed their Indian brothers in a thousand ways. Perhaps Tecumseh lies buried in the land of the Ohio, the land of the beautiful river where he was born. Perhaps the waters of the Wabash sing past his resting-place.

Perhaps the Shawnee know.